# BROADSIDE BALLADS FOR
# CHRISTMASTYDE

## BY BETH BRYANT

**LOU LEAMAN**
MUSIC EDITOR

**BRUCE BRYANT**
BOOK DESIGN

# FOLK WORLD BOOK NUMBER ONE

Folk World, Inc., New York, New York

THIS is a book of traditional Christmas ballads taken, for the most part, from actual ancient broadsides. The book is divided into two sections. The first tells all about the broadsides, the people who composed their ballads, the printers who published them, and the singers who hawked them. The second section is a simple survey of the ballads themselves, relating tales of their origins, growth and personal impact.

From the instant the printing press was introduced into fifteenth-century England, a never-ending parade of print began. Now the village poet, the tavern bard, had a market for his Muse — and with it, became prolific. He adopted the narrative verse style of the Continental troubadour and began producing innumerable ballads. Some dealt with extraordinary occurences, others detailed everyday happenings. If he had little talent for rhyming, he transcribed traditional family ballads, passed through many generations by word of mouth, and sold them to printers for publication. For almost 250 years both the new and old ballads of the English language were committed to print on single-sheet, penny throw-aways called "broadsides," which today form the bulk of source material for English ballad collectors.

The broadside ballads found in this book deal with a very special tradition. Originating in the celebration of that happiest of all "folk festivals," Christmas, they chronicle the myths, philosophies, folk-customs and earthy faith of unsophisticated people. Some of their tunes are the finest in existence, because they are time-tested and purified by persecution. Included are melodies that have lived through wars, plagues and suppression — fighting for survival for almost two thousand years. In singing them, we further their progress. We merge Christmas Present with Christmas Past, creating a precious musical trust for that Christmas Yet To Come.

Beth Bryant

# TABLE OF CONTENTS

# THE
# BROADSIDES

First stands a porter; then an oyster-wife
Doth stint her cry, and stay her steps to hear him;
Then comes a cut-purse ready with a knife;
And then a country client passeth near him;
There stands the constable, there stands the whore,
And, listening to the song, heed not each other;
There by the sergeant stands the debitor,
And doth no more mistrust him than his brother.

Sir John Davies, 1876

# All Men Poor And Humble

All poor men and hum-ble, All lame men who
For Je-sus our trea-sure, With love past all

stum-ble, Come haste ye, nor feel ye a - fraid;
mea-sure In low - ly poor man-ger was laid.

Though wise men who found Him Laid rich gifts a - round Him, Yet
Then haste we to show Him The prais-es we owe Him; Our

ox - en they gave Him their hay; And Je - sus in beau-ty Ac -
ser-vice He ne'er can de - spise; Whose love still is a - ble To

cept-ed their du - ty Con — tent-ed in man-ger He lay.
show us that sta-ble Where soft-ly in man-ger He lies.

**B**allads, my masters, rare ballads! Take a fine new ballad, Sir, with a picture to't." That was the cry of the ballad-singer, the plump farm wench with a husky voice, the wizened old woman who had no teeth, the tattered rake with flashing eyes. In front of the theaters, at the markets, at fairs, bear-baitings, taverns and alehouses, the ballad-singer sang and sold his song. A penny-a-piece was

# Awake Were They Only

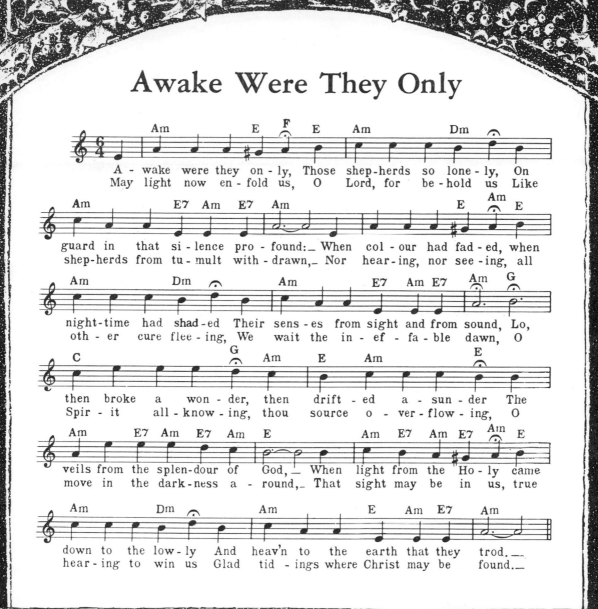

A - wake were they on - ly, Those shep - herds so lone - ly, On
guard in that si - lence pro - found:— When col - our had fad - ed, when
night-time had shad - ed Their sens - es from sight and from sound, Lo,
then broke a won - der, then drift - ed a - sun - der The
veils from the splen - dour of God,— When light from the Ho - ly came
down to the low - ly And heav'n to the earth that they trod.—

May light now en - fold us, O Lord, for be - hold us Like
shep-herds from tu - mult with - drawn,— Nor hear - ing, nor see - ing, all
oth - er cure flee - ing, We wait the in - ef - fa - ble dawn, O
Spir - it all - know - ing, thou source o - ver - flow - ing, O
move in the dark - ness a - round,— That sight may be in us, true
hear - ing to win us Glad tid - ings where Christ may be found.—

the traditional price, and for his hard-earned penny the peasant received one — maybe two — contemporary ballads, crudely printed on one side of a single sheet, topped with a rustic woodcut.

Early on a wintry morning, the balladeer could be seen rubbing his frost-bitten hands outside the printer's door, waiting for his daily pack of broadsides. As he shuffled from foot to foot he glanced

# A Child This Day

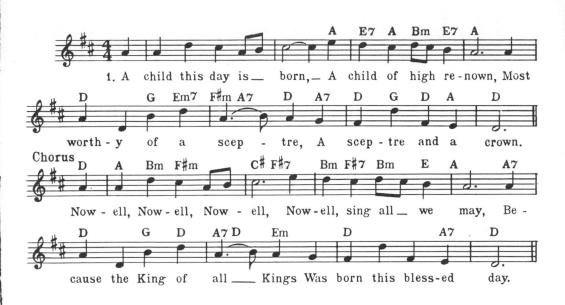

1. A child this day is born, A child of high re-nown, Most worth-y of a scep-tre, A scep-tre and a crown.

**Chorus**
Now-ell, Now-ell, Now-ell, Now-ell, sing all we may, Be-cause the King of all Kings Was born this bless-ed day.

2. These tidings shepherds heard,
   In field watching their fold,
   Were by an angel unto them
   That night revealed and told.

3. To whom the angel spoke,
   Saying, "Be not afraid;
   Be glad, poor silly shepherds,
   Why are you so dismayed?

4. For lo! I bring you tidings
   Of gladness and of mirth,
   Which cometh to all people by
   This holy infant's birth."

5. And as the angel told them,
   So to them did appear;
   They found the young child, Jesus Christ
   With Mary, his mother dear.

over the broadsides on the wall — proclamations, mainly — saying "whale-fins must not be brought into the realm except by the Muscovy merchants," or forbidding the people to "destroy the nests of the queen's swans." If one of the "big-name" ballad-writers should pass, he might shout an amiable greeting and exchange winks with a fel-low singer over just how much ale the printers

# The Cherry Tree Carol

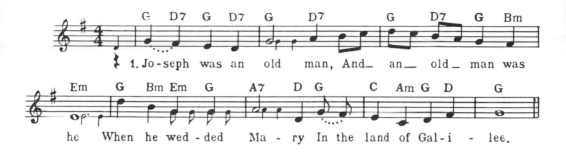

1. Jo-seph was an old man, And an old man was he When he wed-ded Ma-ry In the land of Gal-i-lee.

2. Joseph and Mary walked
Through an orchard good,
Where was cherries and berries
So red as any blood.

3. Joseph and Mary walked
Through an orchard green,
Where was berries and cherries
As thick as might be seen.

4. O then bespoke Mary,
With words so meek and mild,
"Pluck me one cherry, Joseph,
For I am with child."

5. O then bespoke Joseph,
With answer most unkind,
"Let him pluck thee a cherry
That brought thee now with child."

6. O then bespoke the baby
Within his mother's womb,
"Bow down then the tallest tree
For my mother to have some."

7. Then bowed down the highest tree
Unto his mother's hand.
Then she cried, "See Joseph,
I have cherries at command."

8. O then bespake Joseph,
"I have done Mary wrong;
But now cheer up, my dearest,
And do not be cast down.

9. O, eat your cherries, Mary,
O eat your cherries now,
O eat your cherries, Mary,
That grow upon the bough."

10. Then Mary plucked a cherry
As red as any blood;

Then Mary she went homewards
All with her heavy load.

were buying to court *that* writer's Muse. The door opened. Stacks of small song sheets were handed out, and he scanned his day's work.

If there was an earthquake the night before, he would have a mournful ditty to sing, with an exhortation to repentance lest the calamity recur. If there was sports news he might sing "New Song of the Triumphs of the Tilt before the King,

11

# Angels From The Realms Of Glory

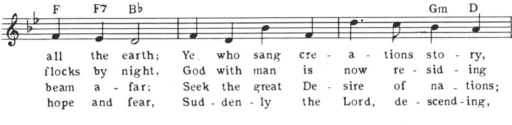

1. An-gels, from the realms of glo-ry, Wing your flight o'er
2. Shep-herds, in the fields a-bid-ing, Watch-ing o'er your
3. Sa-ges, leave your con-tem-pla-tions, Bright-er vis-ions
4. Saints, be-fore the al-tar bend-ing, Watch-ing long in

all the earth; Ye who sang cre-a-tions sto-ry,
flocks by night, God with man is now re-sid-ing
beam a-far; Seek the great De-sire of na-tions;
hope and fear, Sud-den-ly the Lord, de-scend-ing,

Now pro-claim Mes-si-ah's birth:
Yon-der shines the in-fant Light:
Ye have seen His na-tal stars:
In His tem-ple shall ap-pear:

Come and wor-ship,

Come and wor-ship; Wor-ship Christ the new-born King.

the 29th of March, 1604." For broadsides were the
forerunners of our daily newspapers, as well as of
our handbills and circus posters.

Whatever the subject, the singer read the ballad
carefully, searching for a tune to fit its meter and
content — a ballad-air sung by a father or grand-
parent, possibly, one which he could freely alter
to suit his taste. Out into the streets and country

# As I Sat On A Sunny Bank

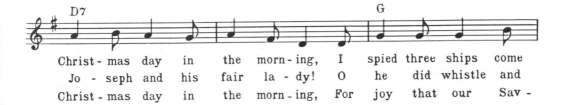

1. As I sat on a sun - ny bank On
2. And who should be with those three ships But
3. And all the bells on earth did ring On

Christ - mas day in the morn - ing, I spied three ships come
Jo - seph and his fair la - dy! O he did whistle and
Christ - mas day in the morn - ing, For joy that our Sav -

sail - ing by On Christ - mas day in the morn - ing.
she did sing On Christ - mas day in the morn - ing.
ior was born On Christ - mas day in the morn - ing.

lanes he went, attracting listeners wherever he stopped.

"Give us a melancholy ditty," a milkmaid cries, and takes it home to charm milk from her cow.

"A love song," murmers a bashful young man, seeking a ballad to woo his sweetheart.

"I like the song well," says the portly town butcher, "but I would have a picture upon it like me."

# All You That Are To Mirth Inclined

All you that are to mirth in - clined, Con -

sid - er well __ and bear __ in mind What

our good God for us hath done, In

send - ing His be - lov - ed Son.

2. Let all our songs and praises be
Unto his heavenly majesty;
And evermore amongst our mirth,
Remember Christ our Saviour's birth.

3. Moreover, let us every one
Call unto mind and think upon
His righteous life and how he died
To have poor sinners justified.

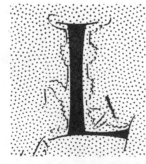

ook you here," retorts the salesman, "here's one as like you as if it had been spit out of your mouth; your nose, eye, lip, chin, sure, they printed it with your face! And the most sweetest ballad that ever I sung."

To the ballad-singer's plaintive voice, at times "as harsh a noise as ever cart-wheel made," the crowd listened, enthralled. He was their source of

# Angels We Have Heard On High

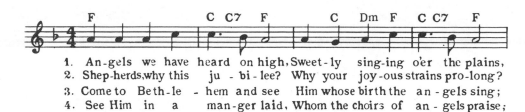

1. An-gels we have heard on high, Sweet-ly sing-ing o'er the plains,
2. Shep-herds, why this ju-bi-lee? Why your joy-ous strains pro-long?
3. Come to Beth-le – hem and see Him whose birth the an-gels sing;
4. See Him in a man-ger laid, Whom the choirs of an-gels praise;

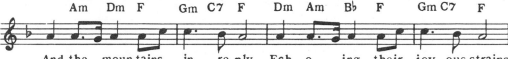

And the moun-tains in re-ply, Ech-o – ing their joy-ous strains.
What the glad-some tid-ings be Which in-spire your heav'n-ly song?
Come, a-dore on bend-ed knee, Christ the Lord, the new-born King.
Ma – ry Jo – seph, lend your aid, While our hearts in love we raise.

Glo - - - ri-a -

in ex-cel-sis De – o, Glo - - -

ri-a in ex-cel-sis De o.

information, of entertainment and edification. If he sang about a Sussex dragon who slaughtered "both . . . Men and Cattell by his strong and vilent Poysin," then, by all means, that dragon existed. If a moralist had written a ballad about a child, recently born, with "a peece of flesh of two fingers thicke" on her forehead, "being wonderfully curled like a Gentlewomens attire . . . a very blew

# The Babe In Bethlehem's Manger

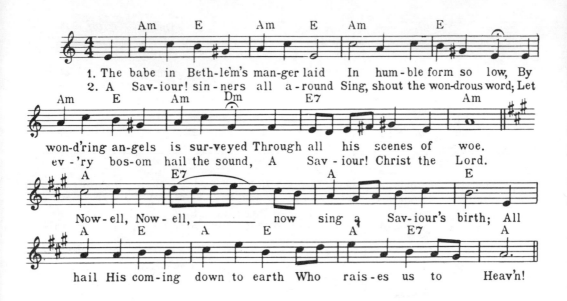

1. The babe in Beth-le'm's man-ger laid In hum-ble form so low, By
2. A Sav-iour! sin-ners all a-round Sing, shout the won-drous word; Let

won-d'ring an-gels is sur-veyed Through all his scenes of woe.
ev-'ry bos-om hail the sound, A Sav-iour! Christ the Lord.

Now-ell, Now-ell, _____ now sing a Sav-iour's birth; All

hail His com-ing down to earth Who rais-es us to Heav'n!

3. For not to sit on David's throne
   With worldly pomp and joy,
   He came on earth for sin to atone
   And Satan to destroy.

4. To preach the word of life divine
   And feed with living bread,
   To heal the sick with hand benign
   And raise to life the dead.

5. He preached, he suffered, bled and died
   Uplift 'twixt earth and skies;
   In sinners' stead was crucified,
   For sin a sacrifice.

6. Well may we sing a Saviour's birth,
   Who need the grace so given,
   And hail his coming down to earth,
   Who raises us to Heaven.

coullour like a turche Locke," then it was obvious that Heaven had condemned excessive display in dress.

Should anyone in the audience be especially moved by a ballad, he might call, "Tell the poet that made it, if he'll come to me, I'll give him a quart of sack to whet his Muse." This was an offer the singer was sure to convey to the writer, after

# The Carnal And The Crane

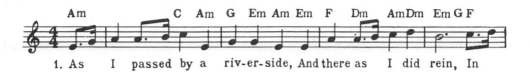

1. As I passed by a riv-er-side, And there as I did rein, In ar-gu-ment I chanced to hear A car-nal and a crown.

2. The carnal said unto the crane,
   "If all the world should turn
   Before we had the Father,
   But now we have the Son."

3. "From whence does the Son come?
   From where and from what place?"
   He said, "In a manger,
   Between an ox and ass."

4. "I pray thee," said the carnal,
   "Tell me before thou go,
   Was not the mother of Jesus
   Conceived by the Holy Ghost?"

5. "She was the purest virgin
   And the cleanest from sin;
   She was the handmaid of our Lord
   And mother of our King."

6. "Where is the golden cradle
   That Christ was rocked in?
   Where are the silken sheets
   That Jesus was wrapped in?"

7. "A manger was the cradle
   That Christ was rocked in;
   The provender the asses left,
   So sweetly he slept on."

work in the alehouse. For the composer and popularizer were on good terms and shared many a two-penny ale. The writer inserted verses in his ballads, inviting tips for singers:

"Thus to conclude my verses rude,
Would some good fellows here
Would join together pence apiece,
To buy the singer beer."

# Gloucestershire Wassail

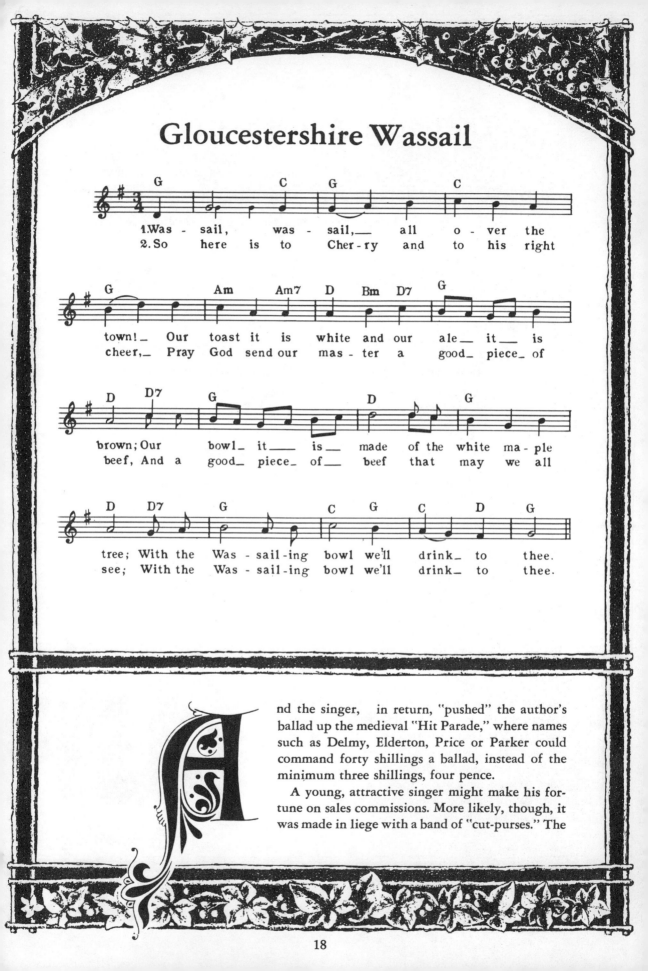

1.Was - sail, was - sail,___ all o - ver the
2.So here is to Cher - ry and to his right

town!___ Our toast it is white and our ale___ it ___ is
cheer,___ Pray God send our mas - ter a good___ piece___ of

brown; Our bowl___ it ___ is ___ made of the white ma - ple
beef, And a good___ piece___ of ___ beef that may we all

tree; With the Was - sail -ing bowl we'll drink___ to thee.
see; With the Was - sail -ing bowl we'll drink___ to thee.

nd the singer, in return, "pushed" the author's ballad up the medieval "Hit Parade," where names such as Delmy, Elderton, Price or Parker could command forty shillings a ballad, instead of the minimum three shillings, four pence.

A young, attractive singer might make his fortune on sales commissions. More likely, though, it was made in liege with a band of "cut-purses." The

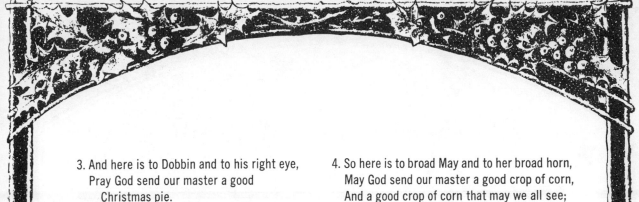

3. And here is to Dobbin and to his right eye,
   Pray God send our master a good
      Christmas pie.
   And a good Christmas pie that may we all see;
   With our wassailing bowl we'll drink to thee.

4. So here is to broad May and to her broad horn,
   May God send our master a good crop of corn,
   And a good crop of corn that may we all see;
   With the wassailing bowl we'll drink to thee.

5. And here is to Fillpail and to her left ear;
   Pray God send our master a happy new year
   And a happy new year as e'er he did see;
   With our wassailing bowl we'll drink to thee.

6. And here is to Colly and to her long tail;
   Pray God send our master he never may fail
   A bowl of strong beer; I pray you draw near,
   And our jolly wassail it's then you shall hear.

7. Come, butler, come fill us a bowl of the best,
   Then we hope that your soul in heaven
      may rest;
   But if you do draw us a bowl of the small,
   Then down shall go butler, bowl and all.

8. Then here's to the maid in the lily
      white smock,
   Who tripped to the door and slipped back
      the lock,
   Who tripped to the door and pulled back
      the pin,
   For to let these jolly wassailers in.

thieves circulated through the absorbed audience, waiting for the balladeer to warn "Beware of cutpurses! Look to your purses!" Unsuspectingly, the simple folk touched their purses for reassurance, signalling their position to the thieves. When the crowd discovered its fleecing, the singer, too, joined in the uproar, bewailing the loss of his purse. Sometimes his fans believed him, sometimes

# Here We Come A-Wassailing

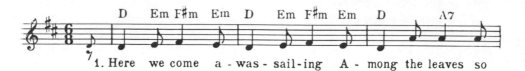

1. Here we come a-was-sail-ing A-mong the leaves so

green; Here we come a-wan-der-ing, So fair __ to be

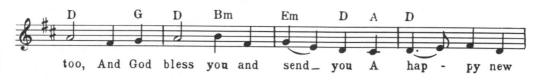

seen: Love and joy come to you And to you your was-sail,

too, And God bless you and send__ you A hap-py new

year, And God send you a hap-py new year. __

they didn't and he found himself rudely flung into the gatehouse.

But if there were singers that were thieves, there were ballad-writers who could be considerd black-mailers, paid *not* to treat a certain topic. Any subject was considered fair game for a ballad and that included, to the dismay of the gentry, town scandals and family skeletons. People of rank and

2. We are not daily beggars
   That beg from door to door,
   But we are neighbor's children
   Whom you have seen before:

3. We have got a little purse
   Of stretching leather skin;
   We want a little of your money
   To line it well within:

4. God bless the master of this house,
   Likewise the mistress, too;
   And all the little children
   That round the table go:

5. Good master and good mistress,
   While you're sitting by the fire,
   Pray think of us poor children
   Who are wandering in the mire:

cultivation dreaded this "yellow journalism." "O to think," cried a Countess, "whilst we are singing the last hymn, and ready to be turned off, some new tune is inventing by some metre-monger, to a scurvy ballad of our death!" Many a person could say on his deathbed, "I'm sorry for one thing . . . that I made not mine own ballad: I do fear I shall be roguishly abused in metre."

# Somerset Wassail

1. Was - sail__ and was - sail all o - ver__ the__ town! The cup__ it is white and the ale__ it is brown; The cup__ it is made of the good__ ash - en tree And__ so__ is the malt of the best__ bar - ley.

1.2.3.5. For it's your was - sail and it's our was - sail! And it's
4. No harm, boys, harm; no harm, boys,__ harm; And a

joy__ be to you and a jol - ly was - sail!
drop or two of ci - der will do__ us no harm.

Yet, the threat of the ballad-writer often acted as "a force for good in the community." A mother used it to control her would-be errant daughter, a small farmer held it over the land-grabber. With Chamont they said,

"I will have thee and thy whole story
Sung to some villainous tune in a lewd ballad;
And make thee so notorious to the world,
That boys in the street shall hoot at thee."

2. O master and missus, are you all within?
   Pray open the door and let us come in;
   O master and missus a-sitting by the fire,
   Pray think upon poor travellers a-travelling
   in the mire.

3. O where is the maid with the silver-headed pin
   To open the door and let us come in?
   O master and missus, it is our desire
   A good loaf and cheese and a toast by the fire.

4. There was an old man and he had an old cow
   And how for to keep her he didn't know how;
   He built up a barn for to keep his cow warm
   And a drop or two of cider will do us no harm.

5. The girt dog of Langport he burnt his long tail
   And this is the night we go singing wassail:
   O master and missus, now we must be gone;
   God bless all in this house till we do
           come again.

Not every ballad tune was "villainous." It was a balladist that wrote the vivid "Cherry Tree Carol:"

> "Then bowed down the highest tree,
> Unto his mother's hand.
> Then she cried, 'See Joseph,
> I have cherries at command.'"

And if the imagery was specific it most likely

# Christ Was Born On Christmas Day

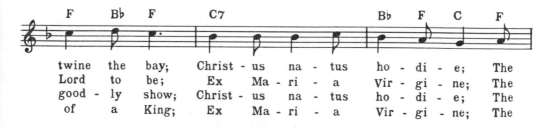

1. Christ was born on Christ-mas Day, Wreathe the hol - ly,
2. He is born to set us free, He is born our
3. Let the bright red ber - ries glow, Ev - ry - where in
4. Christ - ian men, re - joice and sing; 'Tis the birth - day

twine the bay; Christ - us na - tus ho - di - e; The
Lord to be; Ex Ma - ri - a Vir - gi - ne; The
good - ly show; Christ - us na - tus ho - di - e; The
of a King; Ex Ma - ri - a Vir - gi - ne; The

Babe, the Son the Ho - ly One of Ma - ry, of Ma - ry.
God, the Lord, by all a - dored for - ev - er, for - ev - er.
Babe, the Son the Ho - ly One of Ma - ry, of Ma - ry.
God, the Lord, by all a - dored for - ev - er, for - ev - er.

was imprinted on the writer's mind as he viewed church pageants, in this case, *The Coventry Mystery Plays*.

But if a composer did write indecent songs, he also parodied them with "Reproving All Ribald Songs," or "All Ribald and Vain Songs whereof much Hurt to you daily doth come." If he told tales on naughty women, he countered his own

# Come All You Faithful Christians

1. Come all you faithful Christians That dwell here on earth, Come
2. Behold the angel Gabriel, In Scripture it is said, Did
3. Her time being accomplished, She came to Bethlehem And
4. Now to Him that is ascended Let all our praises be; May

celebrate the morning Of our dear Saviour's birth. This
with His holy message Come to the Virgin maid: "Hail,
then was safe delivered Of the Saviour of all men. No
we His steps then follow And He our pattern be; So,

is the happy morning, This is the blessed morn: To
blest among all women!" He thus did greet here then, "Lo,
princely pomp attended Him, His honours were but small; A
when our lives are ended, We all may hear Him call, "Come,

save our souls from ruin, The Son of God was born.
thou shalt be the mother Of the Saviour of all men."
manger was His cradle, His bed an ox-'s stall.
souls, receive the kingdom Prepared for you all.

ballad with "A Godly Ballad declaring by the Scriptures the Plagues that have issued Whoredom." He chronicled miracles and preservations: the prolonged fast of a young maiden who lived for 16 years without taking food or drink, or "A most miraculous, strange, and trewe Ballad, of a younge man of the age of 19 yeares, who was wrongfully hanged at . . . Bon . . . since Christmas

# Come All You Worthy Gentlemen

1. Come all you worth-y gen-tle-men That may be stand-ing by,
2. — Christ our bless-ed Sav - iour Now in the man-ger lay; He's
3. God bless the ru - ler of this house And long on may he reign,

Christ our bless - ed Sav - iour Was born on Christ-mas day. The
ly - ing in the man - ger While the ox - en feed on hay. The
Man - y hap - py Christ-mas - es He live to see a - gain! God

bless - ed Vir - gin Ma - ry Un - to the Lord did say "O we
bless - ed Vir - gin Ma - ry Un - to the Lord did say "O we
bless our gen-er - a - tion, Who live both far and near And we

wish you the com - fort And tid - ings of joy!''
wish you the com - fort And tid - ings of joy!''
wish them a hap - py, a hap - py New Year!

last . . . ; and how god preserved him alive, and brought his false accuser to deserved destruction.''

The customers, interested in miracles and malformations, were even more intrigued by the entertainment news. William Kemp, celebrated comedian and morris dancer, often lamented his difficulties with the men of the Press. He called them "filthy ballet makers," and claimed they were

# The Coventry Carol (Lully Lullay)

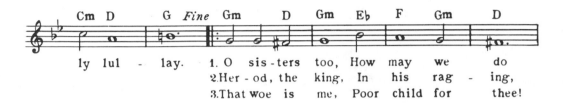

Lul-ly, lul-la, thou ti-ny lit-tle child, By by lul-

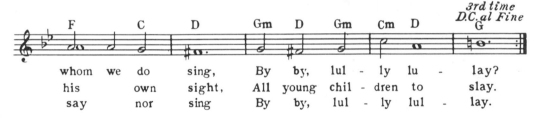

ly lul - lay. 1. O sis-ters too, How may we do
2. Her-od, the king, In his rag - ing,
3. That woe is me, Poor child for thee!

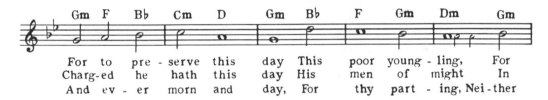

For to pre-serve this day This poor young-ling, For
Charg-ed he hath this day His men of might In
And ev-er morn and day, For thy part-ing, Nei-ther

*3rd time*
*D.C. al Fine*

whom we do sing, By by, lul - ly lu - lay?
his own sight, All young chil-dren to slay.
say nor sing By by, lul - ly lul - lay.

filling the country "with lies of . . . never done acts." He repudiated the ballad of "his entertainment to Newmarket." "Which town," he claimed, "I came never near by the length of half the heath." When starting on a tour with unplanned itinerary, he directed the balladists snidely, "I would wish ye, imploy not your little wits in certifying the world that I am gone to Rome, Jerusa-

# Come Love We God

1. Come love we God! of might is
2. The herd-men came with their off -
3. Three kings came from the east coun -
4. They turned a - gain full mer - ri -

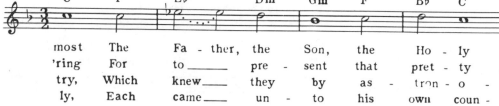

most The Fa - ther, the Son, the Ho - ly
'ring For to _____ pre - sent that pret - ty
try, Which knew _____ they by as - tron - o -
ly, Each came _____ un - to his own coun -

Ghost, Reg - nan - te jam in aeth - e - ra; The
thing Cum gra - ta rev - er - ent - i - a, They
my, Et Be - lam vat - i - cin - i - a; They
try: O De - i mir - a - bil - i - a, They

lem, Venice, or any other place at your idle appoint." Mr. Kemp disdained the ballad maker; others courted him. The young Anne Jeffreys who, in 1696, was fed for six months by fairies, coyly refused to relate her adventures "if she might have 500 pounds for it," appalled at the thought that they "would make either books or ballads" of the tale and spread her name over the countryside.

which made man, both more and less, And
gave their gifts that child un - til They
off - ered him gold, myrrh, in - cense; He
had heav'ns bliss at their end - ing, The

cre - ate him to his like - ness, O quan -
were re - ceived with full good - will; Quam gra -
took them with great dil - i - gence: Quam dig -
which God grant us old and young. De - o ____ Pa -

ta, O quan - ta sunt haec op - e - ra!
ta, quam gra - ta sunt haec mu - ner - a!
na, quam dig - na est in - fant - i - a!
tri, De - o Pa - tri sit Glo - ri - a!

As it proved, a book was written on the matter, which probably pleased the young lady immensely, since it afforded more room than a ballad.

Once he composed the ballad, the author took it to any printer in England and bargained for price. After the printer purchased the ballad, the writer lost all claim to it, regardless of popularity or reprints. Some printers were able to republish

# Dark The Night

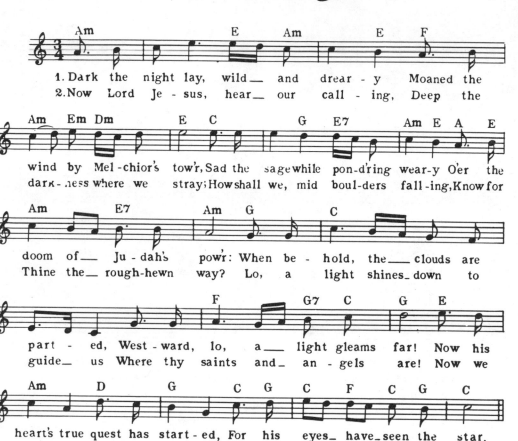

1. Dark the night lay, wild_ and drear-y Moaned the wind by Mel-chior's tow'r, Sad the sage while pon-d'ring wear-y O'er the doom of_ Ju-dah's pow'r: When be - hold, the_ clouds are part - ed, West - ward, lo, a_ light gleams far! Now his heart's true quest has start-ed, For his eyes_ have_ seen the star.

2. Now Lord Je - sus, hear_ our call - ing, Deep the dark-ness where we stray; How shall we, mid boul-ders fall-ing, Know for Thine the_ rough-hewn way? Lo, a light shines_ down to guide_ us Where thy saints and_ an - gels are! Now we know thy love be - side us, For our eyes_ have_ seen the star.

the same ballad for three hundred years, revising spelling, recasting verses, or simply changing the title or date to back the ballad-singer's boast of "absolutely new." The printer was responsible for arranging the copyright. He licensed the song for publication at the Stationers' Company, paying fourpence till March, 1588, and sixpence thereafter. If the clerk remembered to do so, the ballad

# Down In Yon Forest

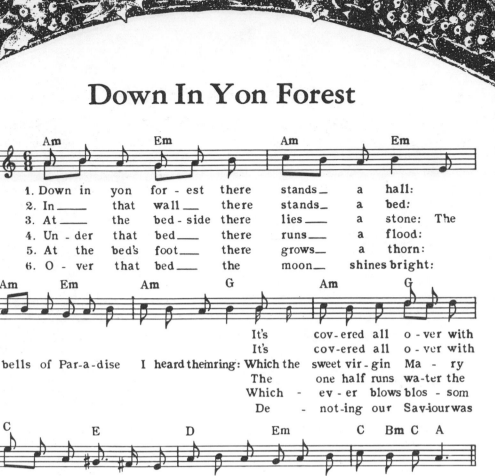

1. Down in yon for-est there stands_ a hall:
2. In___ that wall___ there stands_ a bed:
3. At___ the bed-side there lies___ a stone: The
4. Un-der that bed___ there runs___ a flood:
5. At the bed's foot___ there grows_ a thorn:
6. O-ver that bed___ the moon_ shines bright:

It's cov-ered all o-ver with
It's cov-ered all o-ver with
bells of Par-a-dise I heard them ring: Which the sweet vir-gin Ma-ry
The one half runs wa-ter the
Which-ev-er blows blos-som
De-not-ing our Sav-iour was

pur-ple and pall
scar-let so red:
knelt up-on: And I love my Lord Je-sus a-bove ev-'ry-thing!
oth-er runs blood:
since he was born:
born this night:

was entered in a large register and permission for printing scribbled on the "backside of the written copy." Acting as censor, the Stationers' Company often licensed with the provision "that before the publishing hereof the undecentness be reformed," and if this was not attended to, the ballad was "cancelled out of the book." To get the ballad on the streets while the news was "hot," was the

# God's Dear Son

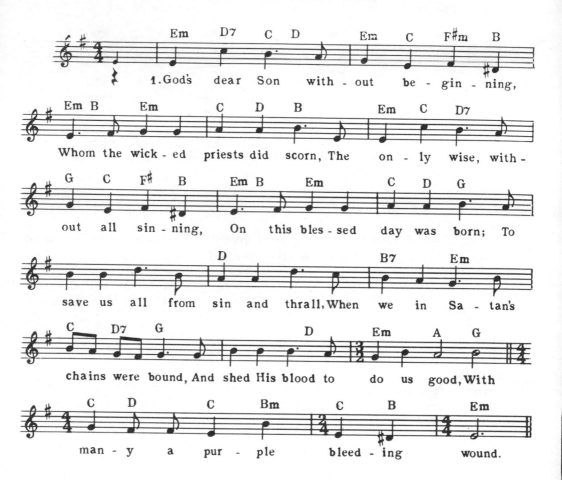

1. God's dear Son with-out be-gin-ning,
Whom the wick-ed priests did scorn, The on-ly wise, with-out all sin-ning, On this bles-sed day was born; To save us all from sin and thrall, When we in Sa-tan's chains were bound, And shed His blood to do us good, With man-y a pur-ple bleed-ing wound.

printer's main concern. He was indifferent to the appearance of ludicrous typographical errors: "he cares not how poorly it be printed, for the faults will be charged to the author." Production costs were low; waste-paper or already pulled proofs were often used. Typesetting was crude; if more than one type was used it was to act as an adver-tisement for the scope of his shop. Ballads were

# Good Christian Men Rejoice

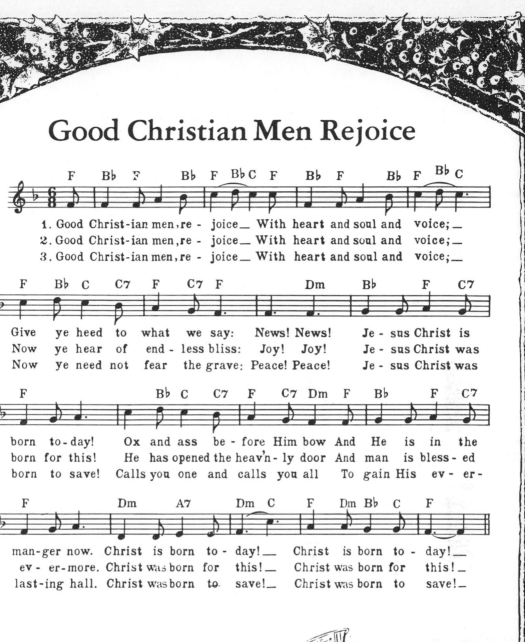

1. Good Christ-ian men, re - joice With heart and soul and voice;
2. Good Christ-ian men, re - joice With heart and soul and voice;
3. Good Christ-ian men, re - joice With heart and soul and voice;

Give ye heed to what we say: News! News! Je - sus Christ is
Now ye hear of end - less bliss: Joy! Joy! Je - sus Christ was
Now ye need not fear the grave: Peace! Peace! Je - sus Christ was

born to - day! Ox and ass be - fore Him bow And He is in the
born for this! He has opened the heav'n - ly door And man is bless - ed
born to save! Calls you one and calls you all To gain His ev - er -

man - ger now. Christ is born to - day! Christ is born to - day!
ev - er - more. Christ was born for this! Christ was born for this!
last - ing hall. Christ was born to save! Christ was born to save!

easy to come by, but the demand for pictures far exceeded the supply. Some printers invested in old collections of worn-out, worm-eaten woodcuts, placing them, regardless of subject, at the top of any ballad. One cut, originally belonging to *Fox's Book of Martyrs,* was used for any broadside lamenting deaths by fire, whether accident or legal execution.

# It Was On Christmas Day

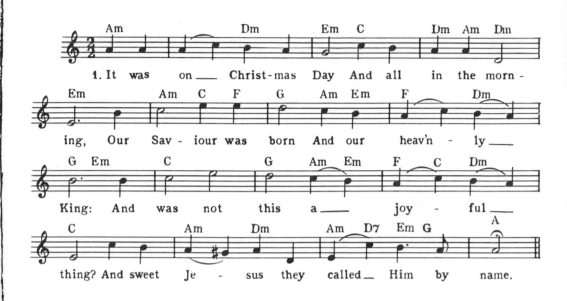

1. It was on ___ Christ-mas Day And all in the morn-ing, Our Sav-iour was born And our heav'n - ly ___ King: And was not this a ___ joy - ful ___ thing? And sweet Je - sus they called ___ Him by name.

2. It was on New Year's Day
   And all in the morning,
   They circumcised our Saviour
   And our heav'nly King:

3. It was on the Twelfth Day
   And all in the morning,
   The Wise Men were led
   To our heav'nly King:

4. It was on the Twentieth Day
   And all in the morning
   The Wise Men returned
   From our heav'nly King:

5. It was on Candlemas Day
   And all in the morning,
   They visited the temple
   With our heav'nly King:

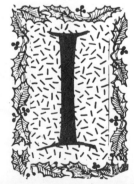

f a ballad already on the market was particularly popular and bringing good profits for a competitor, a printer sometimes "borrowed" several verses to insert in a ballad of his own. The fine for a copyright infringement was not very high, and usually depended on circumstances. In the same year, printer Owen Rogers was fined only twenty pence for printing "half a ream" of

# King Herod And The Cock

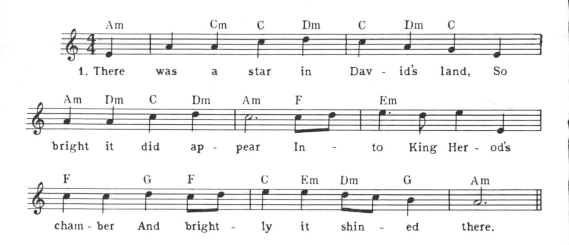

1. There was a star in Dav-id's land, So bright it did ap-pear In-to King Her-od's cham-ber And bright-ly it shin-ed there.

3. "If this be true," King Herod said,
   "As thou hast told to me,
   This roasted cock that lies in the dish
   Shall crow full fences three."

4. The cock soon thrustened and feathered well
   By the work of God's own hand,
   And he did crow full fences three
   In the dish where he did stand.

ballads belonging to another printer, and paid out two shillings for publishing a ballad dealing with Lord Wentworth, who had caused a furore in England by surrendering Calais — clearly, a case of mere violation of law versus offending the Queen and her advisors.

In the frantic competition for fresh news, one printer scooped the market by registering "A

# Let Christians All With Joyful Mirth

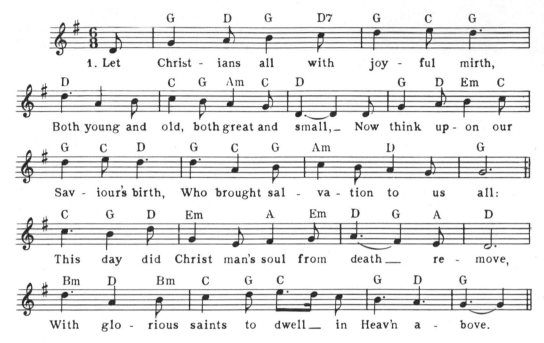

1. Let Christ - ians all with joy - ful mirth,
Both young and old, both great and small,— Now think up - on our
Sav - iour's birth, Who brought sal - va - tion to us all:
This day did Christ man's soul from death — re - move,
With glo - rious saints to dwell — in Heav'n a - bove.

2. No palace, but an ox's stall,
The place of his nativity;
This truly should instruct us all
To learn of his humility:

3. Then Joseph and the Virgin came
Unto the town of Bethlehem,
But sought in vain within the same
For lodging to be granted them:

4. A stable harboured them, where they
Continued till this blessed morn.
Let us rejoice and keep the day,
Where-in the Lord of life was born:

5. He that descended from above,
Who for your sins has meekly died,
Make him the pattern of your love:
So will your joys be sanctified:

Joyful Ballad of the Royal Entrance of Queen Eliz-
abeth into her City of London the — Day of No-
vember, 1588" before the entry had even taken
place. Another technique for cornering the news
was to print a pamphlet on an important event,
such as "The Victory Against Rynebeck, the 20th
of August, 1597," and at the same time license "any
ballad that shall be made thereof." Printers vied

# The Lord At First Did Adam Make

The__ Lord at first did __ Ad-am make Out
(Chorus) Now__ let good Chris-tians__ all be-gin An

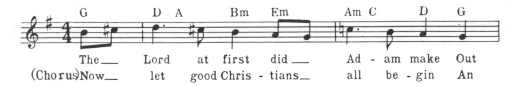

of the dust and clay And__ in his nos-trils__
ho-ly life to live, And__ to re-joice and__

*Fine*

breath-ed life E'en as the scrip-tures say.
mer-ry be, For this is Christ-mas Eve.

And then in E-den's__ Par-a-dise He plac-ed him to dwell, That

*D.C. al Fine*

he with-in it __ should re-main, To dress and keep it well.

with each other for authors whose names had commercial value, carefully keeeping them in ale, for "penny ballads make a better sale than poetry or fiction." Poets who were not so sought after added to their income by writing plays, novels, pamphlets and romances, coaching boy actors or keeping alehouses.

# The Miraculous Harvest

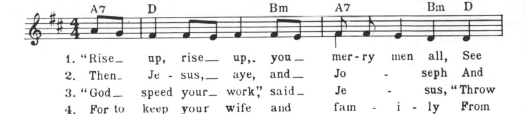

1. "Rise_ up, rise_ up,. you_ mer-ry men all, See
2. Then_ Je-sus,_ aye, and_ Jo - seph And
3. "God_ speed your_ work", said_ Je - sus, "Throw
4. For to keep your wife and fam - i - ly From

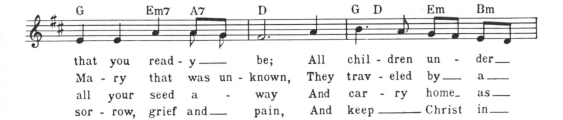

that you read-y ___ be; All chil-dren un - der_
Ma - ry that was un - known, They trav-eled by_ a_
all your seed a - way And car-ry home_ as_
sor - row, grief and_ pain, And keep ___ Christ in_

two years old Now slain they all shall be."
hus - band man, Just while his seed was sown.
rip - ened corn, What you have sown this day."
re - mem - brance Till seed time comes a - gain."

From 1400 to 1647, the making and singing of ballads flourished and broadsides flooded the market. With the advent of Cromwell's Puritan regime, the mirthful ballad was scathingly denounced. Ballad-singers were arrested on sight, dragged into the town square and flogged. Ballads were forced underground, to be sung surreptitiously. Broadsides were sold "under the counter." The cities were silent, but not so the farms. There,

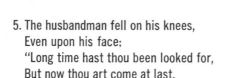

5. The husbandman fell on his knees,
Even upon his face;
"Long time hast thou been looked for,
But now thou art come at last.

6. And I myself do now believe
Thy name is Jesus called;
Redeemer of mankind thou art,
Though undeserving all."

7. After that there came King Herod
With his train so furiously,
Enquiring of the husbandman
Whether Jesus had passed by.

8. "Why, the truth is must be spoke
And the truth it must be known,
For Jesus he passed by this way
Just as my seed was sown.

9. But now I have it reapen
And some laid in my wain,
Ready to fetch and carry
Into my barn again."

10. "Turn back," then says the captain,
"Your labour and mine's in vain;
It's full three quarters of a year
Since he his seed has sown."

11. So Herod was deceived
By the work of God's own hand;
No further he proceeded
Into the Holy Land.

12. There's thousands of children young,
Which for his sake did die;
Do not forbid those little ones
And do not them deny.

the country folk would not surrender either their cherished songs or customs. In the privacy of their own homes, they ignored the indictments of the clergy against music and feasting. They paid little heed to the banning of Christmas, which the Puritan's tagged "Superstitious Man's Idol Day" and "The Old Heathen's Feasting Day."

Annually, the farm folk brought out their yellowed broadsides of the Nativity, the Boar's

# Now The Joyful Bells A-Ringing

1. Now the joy-ful bells a - ring-ing, All ye_ moun-tains,
2. Dear our home as dear none_ oth-er; Where the_ moun-tains,
3. Cold the year, new white-ness_ wear-ing, All ye_ moun-tains,

praise the Lord! Lift our hearts like birds a - wing-ing,
praise the Lord! Glad - ly here our care we_ smoth-er;
praise the Lord! Peace, good-will to us a - bear-ing,

All_ ye_ moun-tains, praise the Lord! Now our fes-tal sea-son bring-ing
Where the_ moun-tains, praise the Lord! Here we know that Christ our broth-er
All_ ye_ moun-tains, praise the Lord! Now we all God's good-ness shar-ing

Kins - men all,_ to bide and board, Sets our cheer - y
Binds_ us all_ as by a cord; He was born of
Break_ the bread_ and sheathe the sword; Brights our hearths, the

voic - es_ sing - ing: All_ ye_ moun-tains, praise the Lord!
Ma - ry_ moth - er Where_ the_ moun-tains, praise the Lord!
sig - nal_ flar - ing, All_ ye_ moun-tains, praise the Lord!

Head, the Cherry Tree legend, for the wassailing custom. With thoughts of maiden's fasts and fairy feasts behind them, with triumphant tilts and royal entries long forgotten, they gathered in the wintry starlight and sang to their welcoming neighbors a "Praise of Christmas:"

"All hail to the days that merit more praise
Than all the rest of the year,
And welcome the nights that double delights
As well for the poor as the peer!"

# ORIGINAL BROADSIDES

**O**ne stretches out his hand, and cries
Come, let me have it, what's the price?
But one poor halfpenny, says I,
And sure you cannot that deny.
Here, take it then says he, and throws
The money. Then away he goes,
Humming it as he walks along,
Endeavouring to learn the song.

The Weekly Register, Jan. 9, 1731

# JOSEPH
## WAS AN OLD MAN.

When Joseph was an old man, an old man was he,
And he married Mary, Queen of Galilee;
When Joseph he had his cousin Mary got,
Mary proved with child, by whom Joseph knew not.

As Joseph and Mary walked the garden gay,
Where cherries grew upon every spray,
O then bespoke Mary with words so meek and mild,
Gather me some cherries, for I am with child.

Gather me some cherries, Joseph, they run so in my mind.
Then bespoke Joseph with words so unkind,
I will not gather cherries; then said Mary you shall see,
By what shall happen, these cherries were for me.

Then bespoke Jesus all in his mother's womb,
Go to the tree, Mary, and it shall bow down,
And the highest branch shall bow to Mary's knee,
And she she shall gather cherries by one, two, and three.

As Joseph was a walking he heard an angel sing,
This night shall be born our Heavenly King,
He neither shall be clothed in purple nor in pall,
But in fine linen, as were babies all.

He never did require white wine and bread,
But cold spring water with which we were christened,
He shall neither be rock'd in silver nor gold,
But in a woollen cradle that rocks on the mould.

Then Mary took her young son and sat him on her knee,
Come tell me, my dear child, how this world shall be;
This world shall be like the stones in the street,
For the sun and the moon shall bow down at my feet.

J. Taylor, Printer, 32, Smallbrook-street, Birmingham.

44

## JOYFUL MIRTH.

Let christians now in joyful mirth,
    The young & old, both great & small,
Still think upon our Saviour's birth,
    Who brought salvation to us all.

And thus our God his son did send,
    Who cruel Jews did hold in scorn,
No pompous train did there attend
    The King of Kings, when he was born.

No place but in an ox's stall,
    The place of his nativity,
Indeed, this should instruct us all,
    To learn from him humility.

'Twas in the city of David then,
    As holy scriptures make appear,
And in the time of taxing, when
    They came both from far and near.

The virgin Mary, then by name,
    And Joseph, most exceeding kind,
When they unto the city came,
    No habitation could they find.

But in a stable, mean were they,
    Continued till the blessed morn;
Let us rejoice and keep this day
    Whereon the Lord of life was born.

Upon this day let none be found
    To practice any idle game,
And though thy mirth should much abound
    In innocence let it remain.

Relieve your neighbours that are poor,
    You are commanded so to do ;
Out of the bounty of your store,
    That they may all rejoice with you.

Thus in your mirth with one accord,
    See that you do all evil shun,
And sing your praises to the Lord,
    For sending his beloved son.

He that descended from above,
    Who freely for our sins has died,
Make him the pattern of our love,
    So may our joys be sanctified.

You that do read these lines, 1 pray
    Let all your hearts be so inclin'd,
To give due honour to this day,
    Which brought salvation to mankind

## THE SEVEN JOYS.

The first good joy our lady had,
    It was the joy of one,
It was to see her own dear son
    Sucking at her breast bone.

The rising of the sun,
    The running of the deer,
The playing of the merry organ,
    Sweet singing of the choir.

Ah, blessed then is our lady,
    And blessed may she be,
For this is one of the seven joys,
    Sprung from our dear lady.

The next good joy our lady had,
    It was the joy of two;
It was to see her own dear son,
    Make the lame to go.

The next good joy our lady had,
    It was the joy of three ;
It was to see her own dear son,
    Make the blind to see.

The next good joy our lady had,
    It was the joy of four,
It was to hear her own dear son
    Reading the Bible o'er.

The next good joy our lady had,
    It was the joy of five;
It was to see her own dear son
    Rise from the dead to life.

The next good joy our lady had,
    It was the joy of six.
It was to see her own dear son
    Wearing the Crucifix.

The next good joy our lady had,
    It was the joy of seven ;
It was to see her own dear son,
    Wearing the crown of Heaven.

J. Taylor, Printer, 32, Smallbrook-street, Birmingham.

## THE SUNNY BANK.

As I sat on a sunny bank,
   A sunny bank, a sunny bank,
As I sat on a sunny bank,
   On Christmas day in the morn-
      ing.

I 'spied 3 ships come sailing by,
   Come sailing by, come sailidg by
I 'spied 3 ships come sailing by,
   On Christmas day in the morn-
      ing.

And who should be with those
      ships,
   With those 3 ships, with those
      3 ships,
And who should be with those 3
      ships,
   But Joseph and his fair Lady.

O he did whistle and she did sing,
   And all the bells on earth did
      ring,
For joy that our Saviour he was
      born,
   On Christmas day in the morn-
      ing.

## HERALD ANGELS.

Hark! the herald angels sing,
Glory to a new-born king,
Peace on earth, and mercy mild,
God and sinners reconcil'd.

Joyful all ye nations rise,
Join the triumph of the skies,
With the angelic host proclaim,
Christ is born in Bethlehem.

Christ, by highest heaven ador'd,
Christ the everlasting Lord,
Late in time behold him come,
Offspring of a virgin's womb.

Veil'd in flesh, the Godhead he,
Hail the incarnate Deity,
Pleas'd as man with us to appear,
Jesus, our Immanuel, here.

Hail the Heaven-born Prince of
      peace,
Hail the Son of Righteousness
Light and life on all he brings,
Ris'n with healing on his wings.

Mild, he lays his glory by,
Born that man no more should die
Born to raise the sons of earth.
Born to give them second birth.

J. Taylor, Printer, 32, Smallbrook-street, Birmingham.

# Christmas Night.

On Christmas night all christians sing
To hear what news the angels bring,
News of great joy, cause of great mirth
News of our dear Redeemer's birth.

And now on earth should men be sad,
Our Saviour comes to make us glad,
From sin and hell to set us free,
And buy for us our liberty.

The King of angels and of men,
The King of kings, of earth, and hea-
    ven ;
Angels and men with joy may sing,
    To see and bless the new-born King.

Now sins depart, behold his grace,
And death, his life comes in his place ;
And now thou may'st thy terrors see,
Thy power great shall conquer'd be.

Angels with joy sing in the air,
For none their ruin can repair :
And prisoners in their chains rejoice,
To hear the echo of their voice.

Now from the darkness we have light,
Which makes the angels sing this
    night,
" Glory to God, and peace to men,
" Now and for evermore," Amen.

J. Taylor, Printer, 32, Smallbrook- street, Birmingham.

# THE
# STAR
OF
## *BETHLEHEM.*

Lo! the eastern Magi rise,
At a signal in the skies :
Brighter than the brightest gem
Shines the Star of Bethlehem.

Balaam's mystic words appear
Full of Light, divinely clear ;
And the import wrapt in them,
Is the Star of Bethlehem.

Rocks and deserts can't impede,
On they press, no guide they need
Day and night, a guide to them
Is the Star of Bethlehem.

Now the holy wise men meet
At the royal infant's feet,
Off'rings rich are paid by them
To the Star of Bethlehem.

Night's terrific shades give way,
Open dawns the promis'd day,
And on us as well as them
Shines the Star of Bethlehem.

Joyful let us quickly rise,
Still the signal's in the skies ;
David's rod of Jesse's stem
Is the Star of Bethlehem.

# The New Star
OF
## *BETHLEHEM.*

When marshal'd on the nightly plain,
 The glitt'ring hosts bestud the sky,
One star alone of all the train,
 Can fix the sinner's wand'ring eye.
Hark ! hark ! to God the chorus breaks
 From ev'ry host, from ev'ry gem ;
But one alone, the Saviour speaks,—
 It is the Star of Bethlehem.
Once on the raging seas I rode :
 The storm was loud, the night was
 dark,
The ocean yawn'd, and rudely blow'd
 The wind that toss'd my found'ring
 bark.
Deep horror then my vitals froze—
 Death-struck, I ceas'd the tide to
 stem :
When suddenly a star arose,
 It was the star of Bethlehem.
It was my guide, my light, my all,
 It bade my dark forebodings cease :
And through the storm and dangers'
 thrall,
 It led me to the port of peace.
Now safely moor'd---my peril's o'er,
 I'll sing first in night's diadem,
For ever, and for evermore,
 The Star !---The Star of Bethlehem !

Joseph Taylor, Printer, 32, Smallbrook-street, Birmingham.

## THE

## THE

# PROMIS'D CHILD.

High let us swell our tuneful notes,
  And join the angelic throng,
The angels no such love have known,
  As we to wake their song.

Good-will to sinful men is shown,
  And peace on earth is given,
For lo! the incarnate Saviour comes
  With messages from heaven.

Justice and grace, with sweet accord,
  His rising beams adorn:
Let heaven and earth in concert join,
  The promis'd child is born.

Glory to God, in highest strains,
  By highest worlds is paid,
Be glory, then, by us proclaim'd,
  And by our lives display'd.

When  shall  we  reach  those blissful
      realms,
  Where Christ exalted reigns?
And learn of the celestial choir,
  Their own immortal strains.

# Holly and Ivy.

The holly and the ivy,
  Now are both well grown;
Of all the trees that are in the wood,
  The holly bears the crown.

The rising of the sun,
  The running of the deer,
The playing of the merry organ,
  Sweet singing in the choir.

The holly bears a blossom,
  As white as the lily flower,
And Mary bore sweet Jesus Christ,
  To be our sweet Saviour.
              The rising, &c.

The holly bears a berry,
  As red as any blood,
And Mary bore sweet Jesus Christ,
  To do poor sinners good.
              The rising, &c.

The holly bears a prickle,
  As sharp as any thorn,
And Mary bore sweet Jesus Christ,
  On Christmas-day in the morn.

The holly bears a bark,
  As bitter as any gall,
And Mary bore sweet Jesus Christ,
  For to redeem us all.
              The rising, &c.

The holly and the ivy,
  Now they are both well grown,
Of all the trees that are in the wood,
  The holly bears the crown.
              The rising, &c.

J. Taylor, Printer, 32, Smallbrook-street, Birmingham.

# THE BALLADS

Be merry all, be merry all,
With holly dress the festive hall,
Prepare the song, the feast, the ball,
To welcome merry Christmas.

And oh! remember, gentles gay,
To you who bask in fortune's ray,
The year is all a holiday —
The poor have only Christmas.

18th Century Broadside

# It Came Upon The Midnight Clear

1. It came up-on the mid-night clear, That glo-rious song of
2. Still through the clo-ven skies they come With peace-ful wings un-
3. O ye be-neath life's crush-ing load, Whose forms are bend-ing
4. For lo! the days are hast-'ning on, By pro-phets seen of

old, From an-gels bend-ing near the earth To touch their harps of
furled, And still their heav'n-ly mu-sic floats O'er all the wear-y
low, Who toil a-long the climb-ing way With pain-ful steps and
old, When with the ev-er-cir-cling years Shall come the time fore-

gold; "Peace on the earth, good will to men From Heav'n's all gra-cious
world; A-bove its sad and low-ly plains They bend on hov-'ring
slow, Look now, for glad and gold-en hours Come swift-ly on the
told, When the new Heav'n and earth shall own The Prince of Peace their

King "The world in slo-emn still-ness lay To hear the an-gels sing.
wing, And ev-er o'er its Ba-bel sounds The bless-ed an-gels sing.
wing: O rest be-side the wear-y road And hear the an-gels sing.
King, And the whole world send back the song Which now the an-gels sing.

Christmas Eve, and the English countryside is blanketed with snow, crisp in the moonlight. Rosy-cheeked youngsters, jostling each other in their rush for a front-line position, cluster outside the window of a well-to-do farmer. Inside, the elders sit warmly around the fire, sharing a wassail toast dipped from "an immense bowl of spiced wine, with roasted apples hissing on its surface."

# O Come All Ye Faithful

O come, all ye faith-ful, joy-ful and tri -
Sing, choirs of an - gels, sing in ex - ul -

um - phant, O come ye, O come_ ye to Beth - le - hem;
ta - tion, O sing, all ye cit - i - zens of heav'n_ a - bove!

Come and be - hold Him, born the King of an - gels;
Glo - ry to God, all glo - ry in the high - est;

O come, let us a - dore Him, O come, let us a -
Ve - ni - te a - do - re - mus, ve - ni - te a - do -

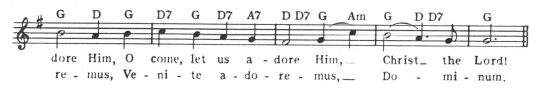

dore Him, O come, let us a - dore Him,_ Christ_ the Lord!
re - mus, Ve - ni - te a - do - re - mus,_ Do - mi - num.

"Good health to you," the literal meaning of the word "wassail," is what they are saying as they raise toasts to each other. Outside the window a sound is heard, a muffled giggle, a soft, "Now!" And a choir of young, wavery voices — almost on pitch — sings out:

"Good Master and good Mistress,
While you're sitting by the fire,

# A New Dial

In those twelve days let us be glad, In those twelve days let

us be glad, For God in His pow'r hath all things made.

1. What are they that are but one? What are they that
2. What are they that are but two? What are they that

are but one? One God, one Bap - tism, and one
are but two? Two Tes - ta - ments,— the old and

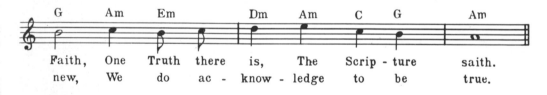

Faith, One Truth there is, The Scrip - ture saith.
new, We do ac - know - ledge to be true.

Pray think of us poor children
Who are wandering in the mire."
Not that they want any misunderstanding as to
their station in life:

"We are not daily beggars
That beg from door to door,
But we are neighbor's children
Whom you have seen before."

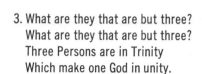

3. What are they that are but three?
   What are they that are but three?
   Three Persons are in Trinity
   Which make one God in unity.

4. What are they that are but four?
   What are they that are but four?
   Four sweet Evangelists there are,
   Christ's birth, life, death, which do declare.

5. What are they that are but five?
   What are they that are but five?
   Five senses, like five kings, maintain
   In every man a several reign.

6. What are they that are but six?
   What are they that are but six?
   Six days to labour is not wrong,
   For God himself did work so long.

7. What are they that are but seven?
   What are they that are but seven?
   Seven liberal arts hath God sent down
   With divine skill man's soul to crown.

8. What are they that are but eight?
   What are they that are but eight?
   Eight beatitudes are there given;
   Use them aright and go to Heaven.

9. What are they that are but nine?
   What are they that are but nine?
   Nine muses like the heaven's nine spheres,
   With sacred tunes entice our ears.

10. What are they that are but ten?
    What are they that are but ten?
    Ten statutes God to Moses gave,
    Which, kept or broke, do spill or save.

11. What are they that are but eleven?
    What are they that are but eleven?
    Eleven thousand virgins did partake
    And suffered death for Jesus' sake.

12. What are they that are but twelve?
    What are they that are but twelve?
    Twelve are attending on God's Son;
    Twelve make our creed. The Dial's done.

The huge front door creaks open, throwing a shaft of warm light on the snow. A plump maid with an apron full of apples, toffee, pennies, maybe, calls out, "Cum on, then," and the shrieking children race up the steps to claim their Christmas bounty.

The custom of wassailing, one of the oldest folk-customs still practiced today, originated in feudal

# On Christmas Night All Christians

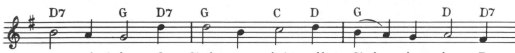

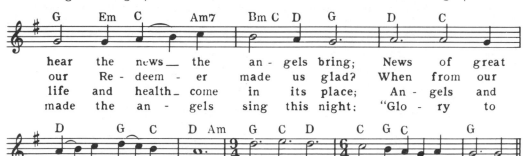

1. On Christ-mas night all Chris-tians sing, To hear the news_ the
2. Then why should men on earth be so sad, Since our Re-deem-er
3. When sin de-parts be-fore_ His grace, Then life and health come
4. All out of dark-ness we__ have light, Which made the an-gels

an-gels bring; On Christ-mas night all Chris-tians sing, To
made us glad? Then why should men on earth be so sad, Since
in its place; When sin de-parts be-fore_ His grace, Then
sing this night; All out of dark-ness we__ have light, Which

hear the news_ the an-gels bring; News of great
our Re-deem-er made us glad? When from our
life and health_ come in its place; An-gels and
made the an-gels sing this night: "Glo-ry to

joy,_ news of great mirth, News of our mer-ci-ful_King's birth._
sins_He set_ us free All for to gain our lib-er-ty?__
men_with joy_ may sing, All for to see the new-born King._
God_and peace to men, Now and for-ev-er-more, A-men.__

days when the tenant, the landlord's liege and servant, was entitled at Christmas to beg in a good-humored way for the alms and food he knew he would receive in excellent measure. Traditionally, the Lords invited the humble people to their manors, where their "waits" or "minstrels" would lead them in "singing for their suppers." The songs they sang were their own, handed down

# Rejoice And Be Merry

1. Re - joice and be mer - ry in songs and in mirth! O praise our Re - deem - er, all mor - tals on earth! For this is the birth - day of Je - sus our King, Who brought us sal - va - tion; His prais - es we'll sing!

2. A heav - en - ly vis - ion ap - peared in the sky; Vast num - bers of an - gels the shep - herds did spy, Pro - claim - ing the birth - day of Je - sus our King, Who brought us sal - va - tion; His prais - es we'll sing!

3. Like - wise a bright star in the sky did ap - pear, Which led the wise men from the east to draw near; They found the Mes - si - ah, sweet Je - sus our King, Who brought us sal - va - tion; His prais - es we'll sing!

4. And when they were come, they their trea - sures un - fold, And un - to Him of - fered myrrh, in - cense and gold. So bless - ed for - ev - er be Je - sus our King, Who brought us sal - va - tion; His prais - es we'll sing!

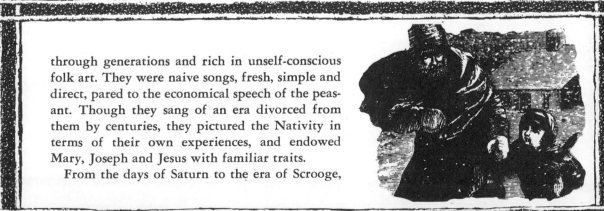

through generations and rich in unself-conscious folk art. They were naive songs, fresh, simple and direct, pared to the economical speech of the peasant. Though they sang of an era divorced from them by centuries, they pictured the Nativity in terms of their own experiences, and endowed Mary, Joseph and Jesus with familiar traits.

From the days of Saturn to the era of Scrooge,

# The First Nowell

1. The first Now - ell the an - gel did say Was to cer - tain pour shep - herds in fields as they lay; In fields as they lay, keep - ing their sheep, In a cold win - ter's night that was so deep. Now - ell, Now - ell, Now - ell, Now - ell, Born is the King of Is - ra - el!

music has been an integral part of the folk-customs of Christmas. The ancient Romans courted Saturn and Ops in song; the Roman fathers of Christianity adapted the practice to praise the Christ Child. The early Christians had their formal, Latin Christmas hymns — some of which survive today. But for the most part their ecclesiastical language was too remote from that of the simple people, to

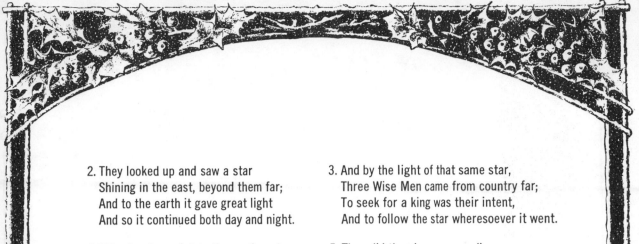

2. They looked up and saw a star
   Shining in the east, beyond them far;
   And to the earth it gave great light
   And so it continued both day and night.

3. And by the light of that same star,
   Three Wise Men came from country far;
   To seek for a king was their intent,
   And to follow the star wheresoever it went.

4. This star drew nigh to the northwest;
   O'er Bethlehem it took its rest,
   And there it did both stop and stay,
   Right over the place where Jesus lay.

5. Then did they know assuredly
   Within that house the King did lie;
   One entered in then for to see
   And found the babe in poverty.

6. Then entered in those Wise Men three,
   Fell reverently upon their knee
   And offered there in his presence
   Both gold and myrrh and frankincense.

7. Between an ox-stall and an ass
   This child truly there born he was;
   For want of clothing they did him lay
   All in the manger, among the hay.

8. Then let us all with one accord
   Sing praises to our heavenly Lord,
   That hath made heaven and earth of naught,
   And with his blood man king hath bought.

9. If we in our time shall do well,
   We shall be free from death and hell;
   For God hath prepared for us all
   A resting place in general.

whom Christmas was not only a religious observance but "a still-living memory of pagan customs, of feasting and other good things of life." Their's was a festival of "clamourous joys and mirth," a season in which to join hands and dance through the streets, singing and laughing with friends.

# Saint Stephen Was A Holy Man

1. Saint Steph-en was a ho-ly man, En-
dued with heav'n-ly might, And man-y won-ders
did he work Be-fore the peo-ple's sight;

**Chorus**

And by the bless-ed Spir-it of God, Which
O man, do nev-er faint nor fear, When

did his heart in-flame, He spar-ed not, in
God the truth shall try, But mark how Steph-en,

ev-'ry place, To preach God's ho-ly name.
for Christ's sake, Was will-ing for to die.

hen the early Christians wended their way by flickering candlelight through the dank catacombs singing, "Glory to God in the highest," they may have given birth to the first Christmas carol in traditional format. A carol was always a processional song; its meter suited the march or dance and, like the ballad, forerunner of our word "ballet," has "dance" at the heart of its meaning.

# Sans Day Carol

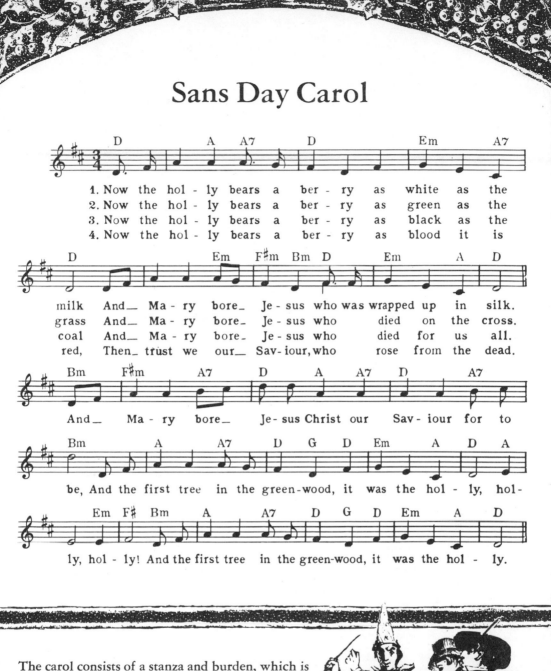

1. Now the hol - ly bears a ber - ry as white as the
2. Now the hol - ly bears a ber - ry as green as the
3. Now the hol - ly bears a ber - ry as black as the
4. Now the hol - ly bears a ber - ry as blood it is

milk And_ Ma - ry bore_ Je - sus who was wrapped up in silk.
grass And_ Ma - ry bore_ Je - sus who died on the cross.
coal And_ Ma - ry bore_ Je - sus who died for us all.
red, Then_ trust we our_ Sav - iour, who rose from the dead.

And_ Ma - ry bore_ Je - sus Christ our Sav - iour for to

be, And the first tree in the green-wood, it was the hol - ly, hol-

ly, hol - ly! And the first tree in the green-wood, it was the hol - ly.

The carol consists of a stanza and burden, which is a type of refrain sung both before and after the verse. The dancers merrily sang and danced the burden, paused and marked time while the leader sang the verse. Through the Middle Ages and especially after the Black Death, peasants danced the carol as an outlet for excess emotions, while the Church, distrustful of its pagan origins, sup-

# The Holly And The Ivy

1. The hol - ly and the i - vy, When they are both full grown, Of___ all the trees that are in the wood, The___ hol - ly bears the crown. The ris - ing of the sun___ And the run - ning of the deer, The___ play - ing of the mer - ry or - gan, Sweet sing - ing in the choir.

pressed all "dance, drama, and communal singing" as distractions from the proper contemplation of sins.

Carols have been variously defined as "cheerful seasonal songs for popular festive occasions," and "songs with a religious impulse that are simple, hilarious, popular and modern." Few carols today can qualify on all four latter counts, but in a

# Unto Us A Boy Is Born

1. Un-to us a boy is born! King of all cre-
2. Cra-dled in a stall was He With sleep-y cows and
3. Her-od then with fear was filled. "A prince," he said, "in
4. Now may Ma-ry's Son, who came So long a-go to
5. O-me-ga and Al-pha be! Let the or-gan

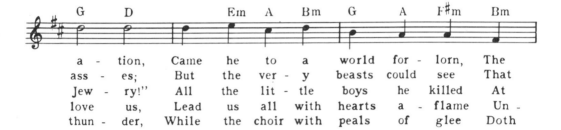

a - tion, Came he to a world for-lorn, The
ass - es; But the ver-y beasts could see That
Jew - ry!" All the lit-tle boys he killed At
love us, Lead us all with hearts a-flame Un-
thun - der, While the choir with peals of glee Doth

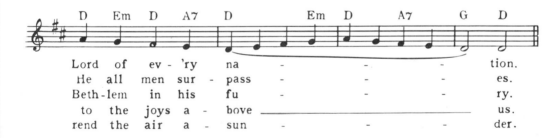

Lord of ev-'ry na - - - tion.
He all men sur-pass - - - es.
Beth-lem in his fu - - - ry.
to the joys a-bove _____ us.
rend the air a-sun - - - der.

medieval manuscript we find headings that read: "Convivial Carols," "Satirical Carols," "Picaresque Carols," "Amorous Carols" and "Humourous Carols."

The ballad was the product of the minstrel, its meter that of the village dance, its purpose to tell a story. Written in lines of fourteen meters, its format was flexible and as many verses could be

# Tomorrow Shall Be My Dancing Day

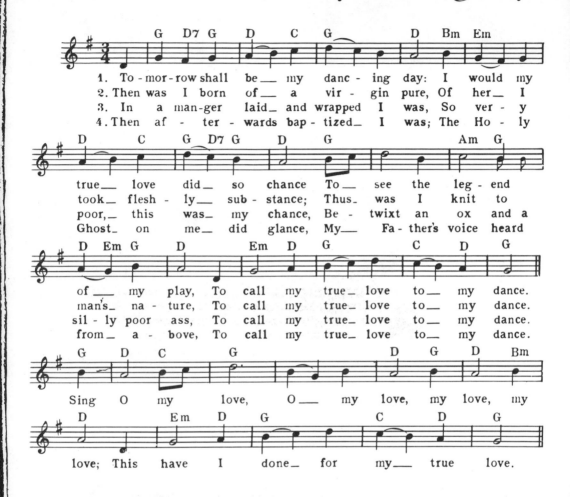

1. To-mor-row shall be __ my danc-ing day: I would my
2. Then was I born of __ a vir-gin pure, Of her __ I
3. In a man-ger laid __ and wrapped I was, So ver-y
4. Then af-ter-wards bap-tized __ I was; The Ho-ly

true __ love did __ so chance To see the leg-end
took __ flesh-ly __ sub-stance; Thus __ was I knit to
poor, __ this was my chance, Be-twixt an ox and a
Ghost __ on me did glance, My __ Fa-ther's voice heard

of __ my play, To call my true __ love to __ my dance.
man's __ na-ture, To call my true __ love to __ my dance.
sil-ly poor ass, To call my true __ love to __ my dance.
from __ a-bove, To call my true __ love to __ my dance.

Sing O my love, O __ my love, my love, my

love; This have I done __ for my __ true love.

appended as folk-singers could rhyme. One ballad, "Robin Hood and his Meiny," boasts 456 stanzas in all. Though the ballad was sung on the Continent during the fourteenth and fifteenth century, it only rose to popularity in England with the advent of printing and the broadside. It was sometime in the fifteenth century that the tradition of the carol crossed with that of the ballad and pro-

PART II

5. Into the desert I was led,
   Where I fasted without substance;
   The devil bade me make stones my bread,
   To have me break my true love's dance.

6. The Jews on me they made great suit
   And with me made great variance,
   Because they loved darkness rather than light,
   To call my true love to my dance.

PART III

7. For thirty pence Judas me sold,
   His covetousness for to advance;
   "Mark whom I kiss, the same do hold,"
   The same is he shall lead the dance.

8. Before Pilate the Jews me brought,
   Where Barabbas had deliverance;
   They scourged me and set me at nought,
   Judged me to die to lead the dance.

9. Then on the cross hanged I was,
   Where a spear to my heart did glance;
   There issued forth both water and blood,
   To call my true love to my dance.

10. Then down to hell I took my way
    For my true love's deliverance,
    And rose again on the third day,
    Up to my true love and the dance.

11. Then up to Heaven I did ascend,
    Where now I dwell in sure substance,

On the right hand of God, that man
May come unto the general dance.

duced a ballad-carol, a popular narrative for seasonal festivities.

One of the most famous ballad-carols, "God Rest Ye Merry, Gentlemen," tells the story of the Nativity as seen through the eyes of the shepherds. Another, "The Cherry Tree Carol," relates a folk legend having no scriptural authority, which gives delicate rustic disguise to Joseph's doubts as to the

# The Holy Well

1. As it fell out — one May morn-ing And up-on a bright hol-i-day, Sweet Jesus asked of His — dear — moth-er If he might go to play. "To play, to play, sweet Je-sus shall go And to play now get you gone; And let me hear — of no com-plaint At night when you come home."

paternity of Mary's Son. In the legendary classic, "The Holy Well," we find a folk-tale of the Boy Jesus going out to play with some town children and being rebuffed for His "lowly birth." In tears, He runs home to Mary and she, pictured as a sharp-tongued peasant housewife, indignantly orders Him to "Take away those guilty souls, and dip them deep in hell." "Nay," smiles Jesus

2. Sweet Jesus went down to yonder town,
   As far as the Holy Well,
   And there did see as fine children
   As any tongue can tell.
   He said, "God bless you every one
   And your bodies Christ save and see!
   And now, little children, I'll play with you
   And you shall play with me."

3. But they made answer to him, "No!
   Thou art meaner than us all;
   Thou art but a simple fair maid's child,
   Born in an ox's stall."
   Sweet Jesus turned him round about,
   Neither laughed, nor smiled, nor spoke;
   But the tears came trickling from his eyes
   Like waters from the rock.

4. Sweet Jesus turned him round about,
   To his mother's dear home went he,
   And said, "I have been in yonder town,
   As after you may see:
   I have been down in yonder town,
   As far as the Holy Well;
   There did I meet with as fine children
   As any tongue can tell.

5. I said, 'God bless you every one,
   And your bodies Christ save and see!
   And now, little children, I'll play with you
   And you shall play with me.'
   But they made answer to me, 'No!'
   They were lords' and ladies' sons,
   And I the meanest of them all,
   Born in an ox's stall."

6. "Though you are but a maiden's child,
   Born in an ox's stall,
   Thou art the Christ, the King of Heaven,
   And the Saviour of them all!
   Sweet Jesus, go down to yonder town,
   As far as the Holy Well,
   And take away those sinful souls
   And dip them deep in hell."

7. "Nay, nay," sweet Jesus smiled and said;
   "Nay, nay, that may not be,
   For there are too many sinful souls
   Crying out for the help of me."
   Then up spoke the angel Gabriel,
   Upon a good set steven,
   "Although you are but a maiden's child,
   You are the King of Heaven!"

through his tears, "For there are many sinful souls crying out for help of me." A tender portrayal of the Child, somewhat reformed from its earlier version, "The Bitter Withy," where, after receiving permission from His mother to go out and play ball, young Jesus invites three "rich young lords" to join Him in a game. Haughtily, they reply,

# Hark The Herald Angels Sing

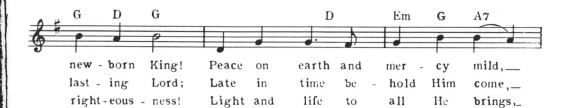

1. Hark! the her - ald an - gels sing, — "Glo - ry to the
2. Christ, by high - est heav'n a - dored, — Christ, the ev - er -
3. Hail! the heav'n born Prince of Peace! — Hail! the Son of

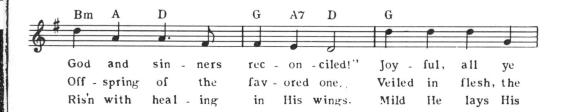

new - born King! Peace on earth and mer - cy mild, —
last - ing Lord; Late in time be - hold Him come, —
right - eous - ness! Light and life to all He brings, —

God and sin - ners rec - on - ciled!" Joy - ful, all ye
Off - spring of the fav - ored one.. Veiled in flesh, the
Ris'n with heal - ing in His wings. Mild He lays His

"We are all lords' and ladies' sons,
Born in our bower and hall;
And Thou art nothing but a poor maid's child,
Born in an ox's stall."
In anger, the hurt Child builds them a "bridge
with the beams of the sun," and when the young
aristocrats rush laughingly over it, they fall into
the water and drown. In anguish, their mothers

na-tions rise;— Join the tri-umph of the skies;—
God-head see;— Hail! th'in-car-nate De-i-ty!—
glo-ry by,— Born that man no more may die:—

With th'an-gel-ic host pro-claim,"Christ is— born in Beth-le-hem!"
Pleased,as man with man to dwell, Je-sus— our Im-man-u-el!
Born to raise the sons of earth; Born to— give them sec-ond birth.

Hark! the her-ald an-gels sing, "Glo-ry— to the new-born King!"

run to Mary, crying,
    "Mary, mild, fetch home your child,
    For ours He has drowned all."
Then Mary — not so mild — calls the Christ
Child home, lays Him across her knee and whips
Him soundly with a clump of green withy twigs.
As the ballad ends we can hear the Boy's bitter
sobs, as He says,

# This Is The Truth Sent From Above

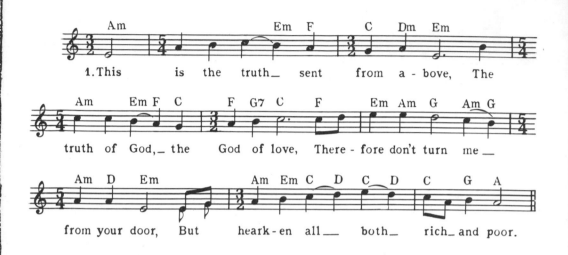

1. This is the truth__ sent from a - bove, The truth of God,__ the God of love, There - fore don't turn me __ from your door, But heark - en all __ both __ rich __ and poor.

2. The first thing which I do relate
   Is that God did man create;
   The next thing which to you I'll tell,
   Woman was made with man to dwell.

3. And we were heirs to endless woes,
   Till God the Lord did interpose;
   And so a promise soon did run
   That he would redeem us by his Son.

4. And at that season of the year
   Our blest Redeemer did appear;
   He here did live and here did preach
   And many thousands did he teach.

5. Thus he is love to us behaved,
   To show us how we must be saved;
   And if you want to know the way,
   Be pleased to hear what he did say.

"O withy! O withy! O bitter withy!
Thou hast caused Me to smart;
And the withy shall be the very first tree
That shall perish at the heart!"

Not all Christmas ballads reflect religious senti-
ments. In a collection of 474 medieval manuscript carols, 77 — about one-sixth — are neither
religious nor didactic. Some are examples of tavern

# The Boar's Head Carol

1. The boar's   head   in hand bear I,   Be - decked with bays and
2. The boar's   head, as I   un - der-stand, Is the rar - est dish in
3. Our stew-ard hath   pro - vid - ed this   In   hon - our   of   the

rose - ma - ry; And I   pray you, my mas - ters   be   mer - ry, *Quot*
all   this land, Which   thus   be-decked with a   gay gar - land   Let
King  of bliss, Which   on   this day   to be   ser - ved is,   *In*

*es - tis   in   con - vi - vi - o:*   *Ca - put a - pri*
*us   ser - vi - re   can - ti - co:*
*Re - gi - nen - si   a - tri - o:*

*de - fe - ro,   Reo - dens   lau - des   Do - mi - no.*

humor, one is a "lying song," a game in which the winner is the one who tells the tallest tale. One carol even warns against trusting women. But the most famous of all secular ballad-carols is one that is still sung annually at Oxford College, in England. "The Boar's Head," originating in the fifteenth century, commemorates the wintry walk of an Oxford student on his way to Mass in Hors-

# God Rest You Merry (Cornwall)

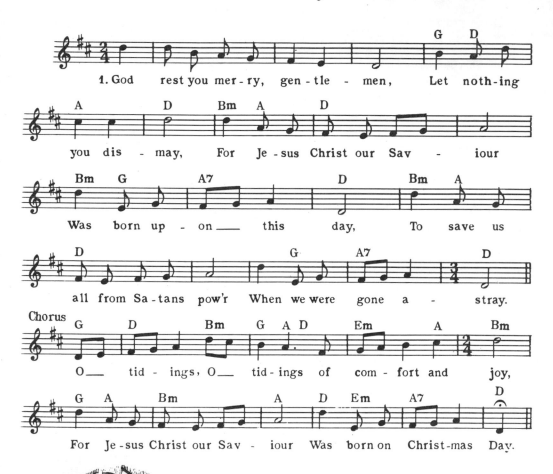

1. God rest you mer-ry, gen-tle-men, Let noth-ing you dis-may, For Je-sus Christ our Sav-iour Was born up-on this day, To save us all from Sa-tans pow'r When we were gone a-stray.

**Chorus**

O tid-ings, O tid-ings of com-fort and joy, For Je-sus Christ our Sav-iour Was born on Christ-mas Day.

path village. The young man strolled along the deserted road, reading a heavy volume of Aristotle, when he was distracted by a sound. Glancing up he saw a wild boar bearing down on him, mouth open and teeth bared for the kill. Instinctively, the student threw his only weapon — the book — at the boar's mouth, where it lodged in his throat, choking the animal to death. With that,

2. In Bethelehem in Jewry
   This blessed babe was born
   And laid within a manger,
   Upon this blessed morn;
   The which his mother Mary
   Nothing did take in scorn.

3. From God our heavenly Father
   A blessed angel came,
   And unto certain shepherds
   Brought tidings of the same,
   How that in Bethlehem was born
   The Son of God by name.

4. "Fear not," then said the angel,
   "Let nothing you afright;
   This day is born a Saviour,
   Of virtue, power and might;
   So frequently to vanish all
   The friends of Satan quite."

5. The shepherds at those tidings
   Rejoiced much in mind,
   And left their flocks a-feeding,
   In tempest, storm and wind,
   And went to Bethlehem straightway
   This blessed babe to find.

6. But when to Bethlehem they came
   Whereat this infant lay,
   They found him in a manger,
   Where oxen feed on hay;
   His mother Mary kneeling,
   Unto the Lord did pray.

7. Now to the Lord sing praises,
   All you within this place,
   And with true love and brotherhood
   Each other now embrace;
   This holy tide of Christmas
   All others doth deface.

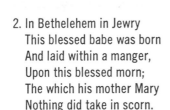

the young man severed the boar's head, placed it upon his staff, and went on to church, leaving his staff on the porch during Mass, and taking the head back to Oxford for dinner.

Ballads that are non-English in origin, filtered into the language and tradition in a variety of ways. The homely tale of "Good King Wenceslas," for example, was brought back to England

# God Rest You Merry (London)

1.God rest you mer-ry, gen-tle-men, Let noth-ing you dis-

may, Re-mem-ber, Christ our Sav-iour Was born on Christ-mas Day To

save poor souls from Sa-tan's pow'r Which had long time gone a - stray,

**Chorus**

And it's tid - ings of com - fort and joy, com-fort and

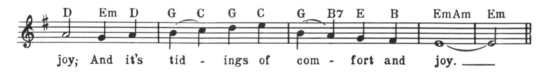

joy; And it's tid - ings of com - fort and joy. ____

by pilgrims who had visited the shrine of his grave. Wenceslas was the first Christian ruler of Bohemia, and a martyr of the tenth century. Numerous tales are told of his gracious treatment of subjects, of how he brought food and clothing to the huts of the poor, adopted stray orphans and found them good homes. The people loved him and willingly followed his gentle lead from pa-

# I Saw Three Ships

1. I saw three ships come sailing in On
Christmas day, on Christmas day, I saw three ships come
sailing in On Christmas day in the morning.

2. And what was in those ships all three
On Christmas Day, on Christmas Day?
And what was in those ships all three
On Christmas Day in the morning?

3. Our Saviour Christ and his lady,
On Christmas Day, on Christmas Day;
Our Saviour Christ and his lady
On Christmas Day in the morning.

4. Pray, whither sailed those ships all three
On Christmas Day, on Christmas Day?
Pray, whither sailed those ships all three
On Christmas Day in the morning?

5. O they sailed into Bethlehem
On Christmas Day, on Christmas Day;
O they sailed into Bethlehem
On Christmas Day in the morning.

6. And all the bells on earth shall ring
On Christmas Day, on Christmas Day;
And all the bells on earth shall ring
On Christmas Day in the morning.

7. And all the angels in Heaven shall sing
On Christmas Day, on Christmas Day;
And all the angels in Heaven shall sing
On Christmas Day in the morning.

8. And all the souls on earth shall sing
On Christmas Day, on Christmas Day;
And all the souls on earth shall sing
On Christmas Day in the morning.

9. Then let us all rejoice amain
On Christmas Day, on Christmas Day!
Then let us all rejoice amain
On Christmas Day in the morning!

ganism to Christianity. His brother, Prince Boleslav, leader of the pagan faction, was intensely jealous of his following. One day he invited Wenceslas to his castle and, despite an old nurse's passionate warnings, the trusting King went. The brothers had just attended services at the castle chapel and were standing on the steps chatting, when two of Boleslav's retainers came up to Wen-

# Good King Wenceslas

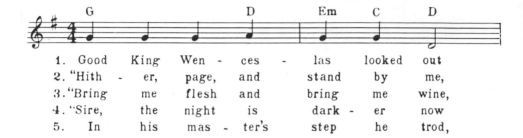

1. Good King Wen - ces - las looked out
2. "Hith - er, page, and stand by me,
3. "Bring me flesh and bring me wine,
4. "Sire, the night is dark - er now
5. In his mas - ter's step he trod,

On the feast of Steph - en When the snow lay
It thou know'st it, tell - ing, Yon - der peas - ant,
Bring me pine - logs hith - er; Thou and I will
And the wind blows strong - er; Fails my heart I
Where the snow lay dint - ed; Heat was in the

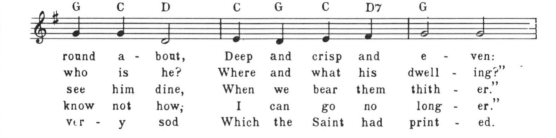

round a - bout, Deep and crisp and e - ven:
who is he? Where and what his dwell - ing?"
see him dine, When we bear them thith - er."
know not how; I can go no long - er."
ver - y sod Which the Saint had print - ed.

ceslas and challenged him with their swords. The King drew his sword, turned his back on his brother, and was holding his own valiantly when he felt a sharp thrust between his shoulders. He turned to see his brother clutching a bloody hilt, fell to the steps, and died. Prince Boleslav gathered his men and rode into Prague to claim the throne, but never the hearts of the people. Not only did

Am   G     D     G    D   Em      C    G     C     D

Bright - ly shone the moon that night, Though the frost was
"Sire, he lives a good league hence, Un - der - neath the
Page and mon - arch, forth they went, Forth they went to -
"Mark my foot - steps good, my page Tread thou in them
There - fore, Christ - ian men, be sure, Wealth or rank pos -

G              D   Em   Bm    C    G    Am  D7

cru - el, When a poor man came in sight,
moun - tain, Right a - gainst the for - est fence,
geth - er; Through the rude winds' wild la - ment
bold - ly: Thou shalt find the win - ter's rage
ses - sing, Ye who now will bless the poor,

G    C    G     D    Em     C       G

Gath - 'ring win - ter fu - el.
By Saint Ag - nes' foun - tain."
And the bit - ter weath - er.
Freeze thy blood less cold - ly."
Shall your - selves find bless - ing.

the Good King's grave become a site for pilgrim-
ages, but the central square of Prague, to this day,
bears his name.

Until the Puritan regime of the seventeenth
century, ballad-carols were produced, published
on broadsides and happily sung by all classes of
people. After the Restoration, they were considered too "rustic," "plebian," by the sophisticated

# A Virgin Most Pure

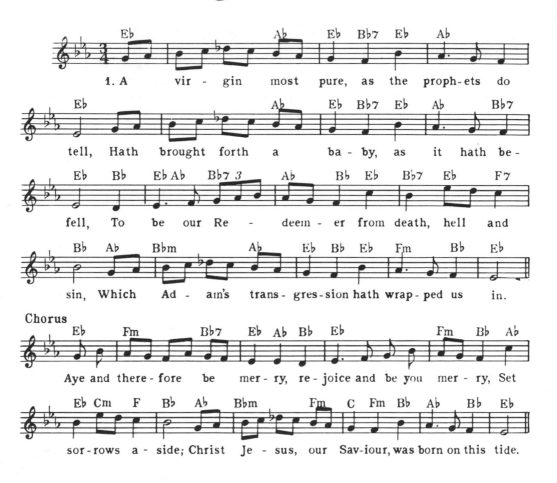

1. A virgin most pure, as the proph-ets do tell, Hath brought forth a ba-by, as it hath be-fell, To be our Re-deem-er from death, hell and sin, Which Ad-am's trans-gres-sion hath wrap-ped us in.

**Chorus**

Aye and there-fore be mer-ry, re-joice and be you mer-ry, Set sor-rows a-side; Christ Je-sus, our Sav-iour, was born on this tide.

urbanites. Left to the care of the farm folk, they were nurtured and preserved, passed from father to son over well-laden Christmas tables and crackling yule logs. When Dickens wrote *The Christmas Carol,* the custom of caroling had vanished from the cities, the ballads had long since retreated to the woods. It was through Dickens' influence that the "old-fashioned" celebration of

2. At Bethlem in Jewry a city there was,
   Where Joseph and Mary together did pass,
   And there to be taxed with many one mo',
   For Caesar commanded the same should be so.

3. But when they had entered the city so fair,
   A number of people so mighty was there,
   That Joseph and Mary, whose substance
       was small,
   Could find in the inn there no lodging at all.

4. Then were they constrained in a stable to lie,
   Where horses and asses they used for to tie;
   Their lodging so simple they took it no scorn;
   But against the next morning our Saviour
       was born.

5. The King of all kings to this world
       being brought,
   Small store of fine linen to wrap him was
       sought;
   And when she had swaddled her young son
       so sweet,
   Within an ox-manger she laid him to sleep.

6. Then God sent an angel from Heaven so high,
   To certain poor shepherds in fields where
       they lie,
   And bade them no longer in sorrow to stay,
   Because that our Saviour was born on
       this day.

7. Then presently after the shepherds did spy
   A number of angels that stood in the sky,
   They joyfully talked and sweetly did sing,
   To God be all glory, our heavenly King.

Christmas was revived, and through the researches of several folk-song collectors, that the ballad-carol was re-introduced into the mainstream of English music. The collectors went into the carpenter shops, the woodsheds and barns of nineteenth century England, noting down tunes of ancient vintage as sung by the reserved farm folk, who so connected carols with the custom of door-to-door

# Remember O Thou Man

1. Re - mem - ber, O thou man, O thou man, O thou man,
2. Re - mem - ber God's good-ness O thou man, O thou man,

Re - mem - ber O thou man, Thy time is spent:
Re - mem - ber God's good-ness And prom - ise made:

Re - mem - ber O thou man, How thou cam'st to me then
Re - mem - ber God's good-ness, How His on - ly Son He sent,

And I did what I can, There-fore re - pent.
Our sins for to re - dress: Be not a - fraid.

3. The angels all did sing,
O thou man, O thou man,
The angels all did sing
On Sion hill:
The angels all did sing
Praise to our heav'nly King,
And peace to man living,
With right good will.

4. To Bethlem did they go,
O thou man, O thou man,
To Bethlem did they go
This thing to see:
To Bethlem did they go
To see whether it was so,
Whether Christ was born or no
To set us free.

singing that, when one elderly man stumbled over some lyrics, another encouraged him with, "Stand up and think you've got snow in your boots, and it'll come to you all right."

The songs the collectors rescued from obscurity were published in several collections, and the survival of the ballad-carol was assured. William Sandys, in 1833, published his book, *Christmas*

# Righteous Joseph

1. When right-eous Jo-seph wed-ded was To
2. "Hail bless-ed Ma-ry, full of grace, The

Is-rael's He-brew maid, The an-gel __ Ga-briel
Lord re-main on thee; Thou shalt con-ceive and

came from Heav'n And to __ the Vir-gin said:
bear a son, Our Sav-iour for to be."

Then sing you all, __ both great and small, Now

well, now well, now well! We may re-joice to

hear the voice Of the __ an-gel Ga-briel.

*Carols, Ancient and Modern,* at a time when "In the metropolis a solitary itinerant may be occasionally heard in the streets, croaking out 'God rest you merry gentlemen,' or some other old carol, to an ancient and simple tune." His sources were "scores of half-penny and penny carols. . . . Several of these carols have woodcuts of the rudest description . . ." And, remarking about such tunes as "The

# The Seven Joys Of Mary

1. The first good joy that Mary had, It was the joy of one, —— To see the blessed Jesus Christ When He was first her son. —— When He was first her son, Good Lord, —— And happy may we be. —— Praise Father, Son and Holy Ghost To all eternity. ——

First Nowell," and "I saw Three Ships," he said they are "of a pleasing and plaintive nature, and most of them appear to be of considerable antiquity." He included six French Noëls in his book of carols, and various other volumes included popular ballads from Germany, Sweden, Wales, and other countries within the realm of Christianity, establishing a world-wide heritage of seasonal

2. The next good joy that Mary had,
   It was the joy of two,
   To see her own son Jesus Christ
   Make the lame to go,
   Make the lame to go, good Lord,
   And happy may we be.
   Praise Father, Son and Holy Ghost
   To all eternity.

3. The next good joy that Mary had,
   It was the joy of three,
   To see her own son Jesus Christ
   Make the blind to see,
   Make the blind to see, good Lord,
   And happy may we be.
   Praise Father, Son and Holy Ghost
   To all eternity.

4. The next good joy that Mary had,
   It was the joy of four,
   To see her own son Jesus Christ
   Read the bible o'er,
   Read the bible o'er, good Lord,
   And happy may we be.
   Praise Father, Son and Holy Ghost
   To all eternity.

5. The next good joy that Mary had,
   It was the joy of five,
   To see her own son Jesus Christ
   Raise the dead to life,
   Raise the dead to life, good Lord,
   And happy may we be.
   Praise Father, Son and Holy Ghost
   To all eternity.

6. The next good joy that Mary had,
   It was the joy of six,
   To see her own son Jesus Christ
   Upon the crucifix,
   Upon the crucifix, good Lord,
   And happy may we be.
   Praise Father, Son and Holy Ghost
   To all eternity.

7. The next good joy that Mary had,
   It was the joy of seven,
   To see her own son Jesus Christ
   Ascending in to Heav'n,
   Ascending in to Heav'n, good Lord,
   And happy may we be.
   Praise Father, Son and Holy Ghost
   To all eternity.

music — one which can cross even barriers of national differences, to make peace between men.

On the day before Christmas, 1914, the first winter of World War I, soldiers huddled dismally together in trenches, Germans on one side, British on the other, a waste of no man's land, scattered with bodies, between them. A young, blond soldier, reloading his gun, thought wistfully of home

# The Seven Virgins

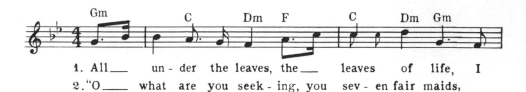

1. All___ un - der the leaves, the___ leaves of life, I
2. "O ___ what are you seek - ing, you sev - en fair maids,

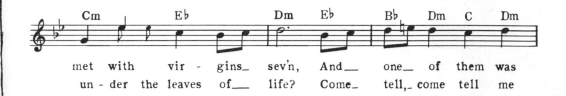

met with vir - gins_ sev'n, And___ one_ of them was
un - der the leaves of_ life? Come_ tell,_ come tell me

Ma - ry mild, Our___ Lord's_ moth - er___ from heav'n.
what seek you All ___ un - der the leaves_ of life?"

3. "We're seeking for no leaves, Thomas,
But for a friend of thine;
We're seeking for sweet Jesus Christ
To be our guide and thine."

4. "Go you down, go you down to yonder town
And sit in the gallery
And there you'll find sweet Jesus Christ
Nailed to a big yew-trée."

in Berlin, where his plump, smiling mother would be basting the fowls, and his small brothers anxiously awaiting their gifts. Softly, under his breath, the homesick lad hummed a tune of his childhood, aimed his gun and fired. The dark, wiry man beside him turned and smiled, picked up the tune and sang a few words. Words passed from man to man and the entire trench was filled

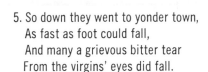

5. So down they went to yonder town,
   As fast as foot could fall,
   And many a grievous bitter tear
   From the virgins' eyes did fall.

6. "O peace, mother, O peace, mother;
   Your weeping doth me grieve;
   O I must suffer this," he said,
   "For Adam and for Eve."

7. "O how can I my weeping leave,
   Or my sorrows undergo,
   Whilst I do see my own Son die,
   When sons I have no mo'?"

8. "Dear mother, dear mother, you must take John
   All for to be your son;
   And he will comfort you sometimes,
   Mother, as I have done."

9. "O come, thou John Evangelist,
   Thou'rt welcome unto me,
   But more welcome my own dear son,
   That I nursed upon my knee."

10. Then he laid his head on his right shoulder,
    Seeing death it struck him nigh;
    "The Holy Ghost be with your soul;
    I die, mother dear, I die."

11. O the rose, the rose, the gentle rose
    And the fennel that grows so green!
    God give us grace in every place
    To pray for our king and queen.

12. Furthermore for our enemies all
    Our prayers they should be strong.
    Amen, good Lord! your charity
    Is the ending of my song.

with the sound of "Stille Nacht."

Across in the British trenches, a strain of distant singing could be heard between volleys of bullets. A teen-age volunteer, streaked with dirt, stopped in amazement as he recognized the tune. "I say," he whispered, "It's 'Silent Night'!" And sang, softly and ironically, "All is calm, all is bright."

# The Shepherds Amazed

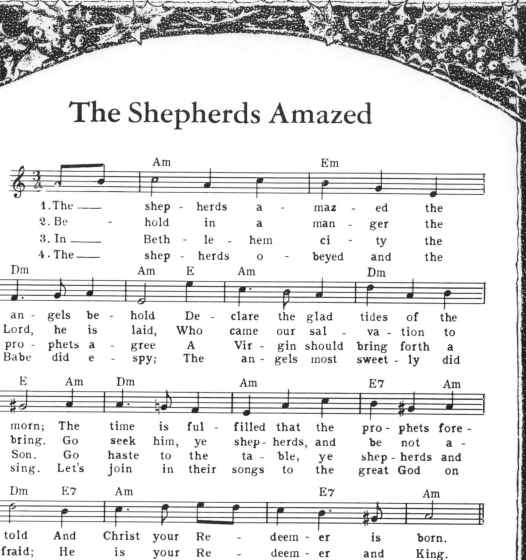

| | Am | Em |
|---|---|---|
| 1. The ___ | shep - herds a - | maz - ed the |
| 2. Be - | hold in a | man - ger the |
| 3. In ___ | Beth - le - hem | ci - ty the |
| 4. The ___ | shep - herds o - | beyed and the |

Dm — Am E Am — Dm

| an - gels be - hold | De - clare the glad | tides of the |
| Lord, he is laid, | Who came our sal - | va - tion to |
| pro - phets a - gree | A Vir - gin should | bring forth a |
| Babe did e - spy; | The an - gels most | sweet - ly did |

E Am Dm — Am — E7 Am

| morn; The time is ful - | filled that the | pro - phets fore - |
| bring. Go seek him, ye | shep - herds, and | be not a - |
| Son. Go haste to the | ta - ble, ye | shep - herds and |
| sing. Let's join in their | songs to the | great God on |

Dm E7 Am — E7 Am

| told And Christ your Re - | deem - er is born. |
| fraid; He is your Re - | deem - er and King. |
| see, For as it was | said it is done. |
| high For send - ing our | Sav - iour and King. |

Quickly, the song darted from trench to trench, the familiar tune, the gentle words criss-crossing no-man's land till no shooting could be heard, only the sound of men's voices joined in song. A peaked khaki cap appeared over a mound of dirt; tentatively, a spiked helmet emerged from an opposite trench. Neither man fired. Other heads rose above ground level, then shoulders and arms, till men

All glo - ry and hon - our to God, our Cre - a - tor, Who came from His glo - ry on high; In hum - ble sub - mis - sion took on Him our na - ture, That we might par - take of His joy.

tumbled out of their foxholes, over the barbed wire and onto the hard-packed earth that separated the forces.

Alarmed, the officers rushed through their troops yelling, "Get back there!" But met with only a pathetic, "Aw, but it's Christmas, ain't it?"

German greeted Englishman with a handshake, and together they buried their dead. Then, gifts

# While Shepherds Watched Their Flocks

1. While shep-herds watched their flocks by night, All seat - ed on the
2. To you in Dav - id's town this day Is born of Dav-id's
3. Thus spake the Ser - aph: and forth-with Ap-peared a shin-ing

ground, The An - gel of the Lord came down And glo - ry shone a -
line A Sav - iour, who is Christ the Lord: And this shall be the
throng Of an - gels prais - ing God, who thus Ad - dressed their joy-ful

round. "Fear not," said he (for might - y dread Had seized their trou - bled
sign: The heav'n - ly Babe you there shall find To hu - man view dis-
song: "All glo - ry be to God on high And to the earth be

mind)"Glad tid - ings of great joy I bring To you and all man - kind.
played, All mean - ly wrapped in swath-ing bands And in a man-ger laid."
peace; Good - will hence-forth from heav'n to men Be-gin, and nev-er cease."

were exchanged, the Germans sharing their traditional Christmas cakes, *Weinachtskrapfen,* and
the British boys giving up plum puddings baked
by wives and sweethearts at home. Some of the
soldiers marked off a stretch of no man's land to
resemble a football field and chose up sides for
a game. Others snapped pictures, walked — arms
about shoulders—discussing common interests, and

# Silent Night

1. Si - lent night! Ho - ly night! All is calm
2. Si - lent night! Ho - ly night! Shep - herds quake
3. Si - lent night! Ho - ly night! Son of God,

all is bright Round yon vir - gin moth - er and Child!
at the sight! Glo - ries stream_ from heav - en a - far,
Love's pure light Rad - iant beams_ from Thy ho - ly face,

Ho - ly In - fant, so ten - der and mild, Sleep in heav - en - ly
Heav'n - ly hosts_ sing Al - le - lu - ia, Christ, the Sav - iour, is
With the dawn of re - deem - ing grace, Je - sus, Lord, at Thy

peace,_____ Sleep ____ in heav - en - ly peace.
born! _____ Christ, ____ the Sav - iour, is born!
birth, _____ Je - sus, Lord, at Thy birth.

made faltering attempts at each other's language.

From Christmas Eve to Christmas night, the un-signed armistice was in effect. At sunset, Christmas Day, the soldiers were herded back to their trenches. Each side fired a warning shot, and the business of killing one another was resumed. For one day soldiers had become men, under the in-fluence of a simple song, proving, to quote Ogden

# We Three Kings Of Orient Are

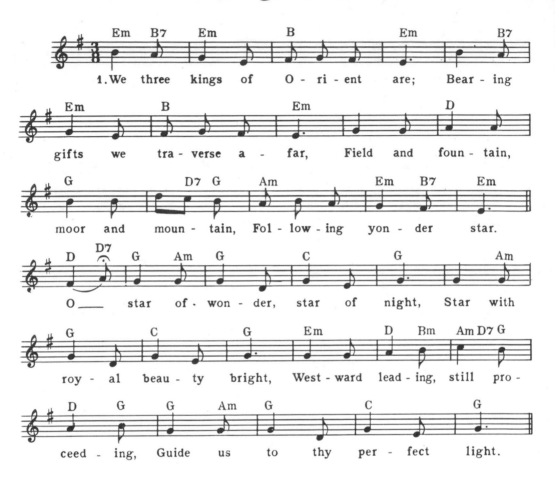

1. We three kings of O - ri - ent are; Bear - ing
gifts we tra - verse a - far, Field and foun - tain,
moor and moun - tain, Fol - low - ing yon - der star.
O ___ star of - won - der, star of night, Star with
roy - al beau - ty bright, West - ward lead - ing, still pro -
ceed - ing, Guide us to thy per - fect light.

Nash, that
"people can't concentrate properly on blowing other
people to pieces properly if their minds are poisoned by thoughts suitable to the twenty-fifth of December."
Along with the twentieth century, come contemporary carols dealing with present-day prob-

(Gaspar)

2. Born a King on Bethlehem plain,
   Gold I bring to crown Him again,
   King forever, ceasing never,
   Over us all to reign.

(Balthasar)

4. Myrrh is mine; its bitter perfume
   Breathes a life of gathering gloom;
   Sorrowing, sighing, bleeding, dying,
   Sealed in the stone-cold tomb.

(Melchior)

3. Frankincense to offer have I,
   Incense owns a Deity nigh:
   Prayer and praising all men raising,
   Worship Him, God on high.

(All)

5. Glorious now behold Him arise,
   King and God and sacrifice;
   Heav'n sings Alleluia:
   Alleluia the earth replies.

lems. The yearning for peace and world unity is expressed by folk groups singing, "Why can't we have Christmas the whole year around?" Tom Lehrer, modern minstrel in Ivy League suit, protests the growth of Christmas commercialism with the parody, "Hark the Herald Tribune sings, advertising wondrous things!" — a warning that the "Ballad of Bond Street" is outshouting that of

# O Little Town Of Bethlehem

1. O lit - tle town of Beth - le - hem, How still we__ see thee lie! A - bove thy deep and dream - less sleep The si - lent__ stars go by. Yet in thy dark streets shin - eth The ev - er - last - ing light; The hopes and fears of all the years Are met in thee to - night.

Bethlehem and the click of the cash register has drowned out the cry of the Babe. Cynics, claiming that Christmas has been negated by such commercialism, much in the spirit of the solemn medieval clergy and the Puritan of the renaissance, call for its abolishment.

Yet, the people, unmindful of critical voices, rush out to the super market to purchase plump

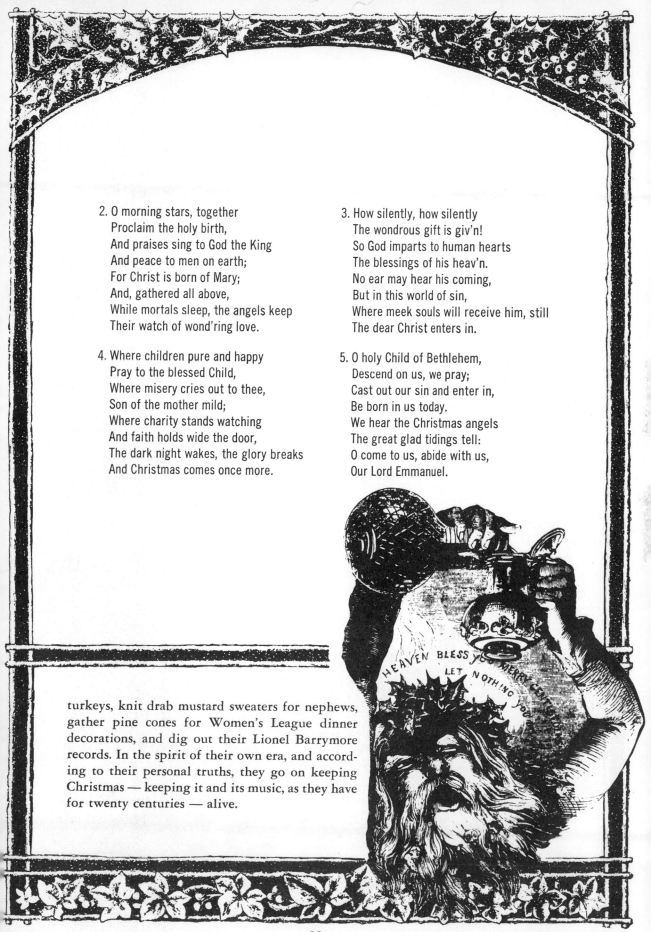

2. O morning stars, together
   Proclaim the holy birth,
   And praises sing to God the King
   And peace to men on earth;
   For Christ is born of Mary;
   And, gathered all above,
   While mortals sleep, the angels keep
   Their watch of wond'ring love.

3. How silently, how silently
   The wondrous gift is giv'n!
   So God imparts to human hearts
   The blessings of his heav'n.
   No ear may hear his coming,
   But in this world of sin,
   Where meek souls will receive him, still
   The dear Christ enters in.

4. Where children pure and happy
   Pray to the blessed Child,
   Where misery cries out to thee,
   Son of the mother mild;
   Where charity stands watching
   And faith holds wide the door,
   The dark night wakes, the glory breaks
   And Christmas comes once more.

5. O holy Child of Bethlehem,
   Descend on us, we pray;
   Cast out our sin and enter in,
   Be born in us today.
   We hear the Christmas angels
   The great glad tidings tell:
   O come to us, abide with us,
   Our Lord Emmanuel.

turkeys, knit drab mustard sweaters for nephews, gather pine cones for Women's League dinner decorations, and dig out their Lionel Barrymore records. In the spirit of their own era, and according to their personal truths, they go on keeping Christmas — keeping it and its music, as they have for twenty centuries — alive.

# Sussex Mummer's Carol

1. O mor-tal man, re - mem-ber well When Christ our Lord was
2. O mor-tal man, re - mem-ber well When Christ died on the

born; He was cru - ci - fied be - tween two thieves And
rood; 'Twas for our sins and wick - ed ways Christ

crowned-ed with the thorn, — And crown - ed with — the thorn.
shed His pre-cious blood, — Christ shed — His pre - cious blood.

3. O mortal man, remember well
   When Christ was wrapped in clay;
   He was taken to a sepulchre
   Where no man ever lay.

4. God bless the mistress of this house
   With gold chain round her breast;
   Where e'er her body sleeps or wakes,
   Lord, send her soul to rest.

5. God bless the master of this house
   With happiness beside;
   Where e'er his body rides or walks
   Lord Jesus be his guide.

6. God bless your house, your children, too,
   Your cattle and your store;
   The Lord increase you day by day
   And send you more and more.

# SOURCES

ALL ABOUT CHRISTMAS, M. Krythe, 1954
AMERICAN BALLADRY FROM BRITISH BROADSIDES, G. Laws, 1957
THE BALLAD TREE, E. Wells, 1950
THE BLACK-LETTER BROADSIDE BALLAD, H. Rollins, 1919
THE BOOK OF CHRISTMAS, H. Mabie, 1909
THE BROADSIDE BALLAD, L. Shepard, 1962
A CHRISTMAS BOOK, D. Lewis and G. Heseltine, 1928
CHRISTMAS SONGS AND THEIR STORIES, H. Wernecke, 1957
CHRISTMAS TRADITIONS, W. Auld, 1942
THE EARLY ENGLISH CAROLS, R. Greene, 1935
THE ENGLISH CAROL, E. Routley, 1958
ENGLISH FOLK-CAROLS, C. Sharp, 1911
ENGLISH TRADITIONAL SONGS AND CAROLS, L. Broadwood, 1908
HOBBIES, "Song Broadsides," W. McDevitt, 1938-39
INTERNATIONAL CONGRESS OF MUSICOLOGY PAPERS, "Broadside Ballads," R. Lamson, 1939
1001 CHRISTMAS FACTS AND FANCIES, A. Hottes, 1938
THE OXFORD BOOK OF CAROLS, P. Dearmer, R. Williams and M. Shaw, 1928
A PARTRIDGE IN A PEAR TREE, N. Braybrooke, 1960
SOME FORERUNNERS OF THE NEWSPAPER IN ENGLAND 1476-1622, M. Shaaber, 1929
A TREASURY OF CHRISTMAS SONGS AND CAROLS, H. Simon, 1955
THE TWELVE DAYS OF CHRISTMAS, M. and J. Hadfield, 1961
UNDER THE GREENWOOD TREE, T. Hardy, 1873